1 Dot to dot

Starting with number 1, draw a line to join the dots and complete the picture.

2 Hey diddle, diddle

Finish the nursery rhyme by writing the missing words in the spaces.

Hey diddle, diddle,

The cat and the fiddle,

The cow jumped over the moon,

The little _ _ _ laughed to see such fun,

And the _ _ _ _ ran away with

the _ _ _ _ _.

③ Maze

Help the children find their way out of the maze.

4 Math puzzle

Do the math in the grid by filling in the missing numbers.

2	+	2	=	
+	■	−	■	+
	−	2	=	7
=	■	=	■	=
11	+		=	11

5 Hidden word

Cross out the letters that appear twice in the grid.
The letters that are left spell a type of pet.

K	H	C	Z	P
Q	R	O	Q	M
R	F	U	I	O
A	H	M	U	F
P	I	K	Z	T

6 How many?

How many new words can you make
from the word skeleton?

SKELETON

7 Color by numbers

Color this picture by using the number key. Then color the rest of the picture.

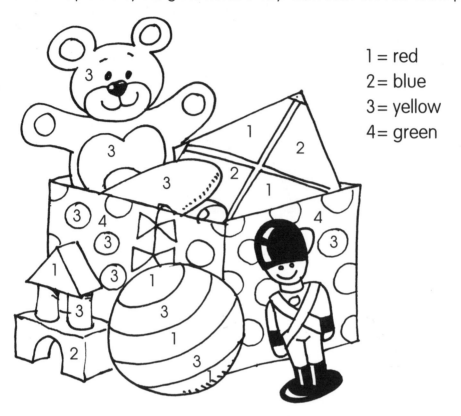

1 = red
2 = blue
3 = yellow
4 = green

8 Reveal the picture

Shade in all the spaces marked with a dot to reveal the picture.

⑨ **Wordsearch**

Look in the wordsearch grid for the names of eight buildings. You will find them by reading across or down. Circle the words.

```
Q  W  C  H  U  R  C  H  L
T  J  B  O  D  V  D  X  I
O  S  Z  U  A  F  B  J  G
W  C  P  S  K  J  A  R  H
E  H  V  E  S  E  R  C  T
R  O  X  R  B  H  N  T  H
C  O  T  T  A  G  E  O  O
J  L  A  M  L  H  T  D  U
D  K  T  V  V  N  U  G  S
W  L  R  C  A  S  T  L  E
```

10 Word trail

Use the picture clues to fill in the word trail – the last letter of each word is the first letter of the next.

11 Wiggly worm

Which wormhole leads to the flower bed?

12 Trivia quiz

Who invented television?

a) John Logie Baird
b) James Bond
c) Isaac Newton

13 What do they do?

Draw lines to match people with their jobs.

gardener

teacher

doctor

14 Scrambled words

Can you unscramble these words? They are all things that you might find in a garden.

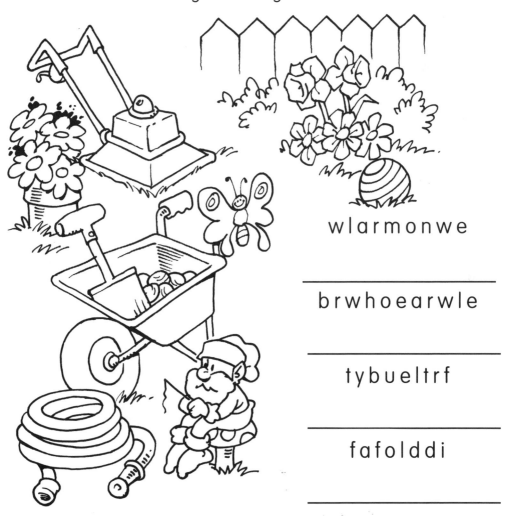

w l a r m o n w e

_____

b r w h o e a r w l e

_____

t y b u e l t r f

_____

f a f o l d d i

_____

15 Silhouettes

Look carefully at the silhouettes. Write what they are on the lines below.

_____   _____   _____

16 Match the shoes

Draw a line to connect the matching pair of shoes.

a

b

c

d

e

f

17 Jigsaw pieces

Draw lines to connect the jigsaw pieces that go together
to make three pictures.

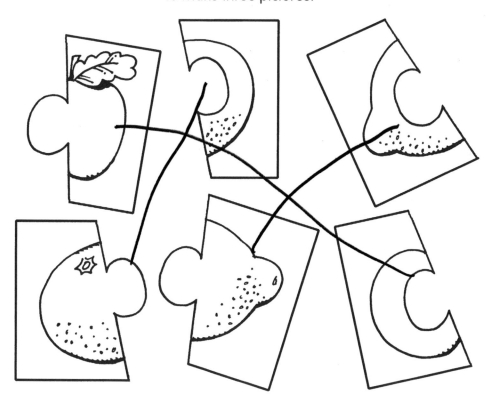

18 **Spot the difference**

Look carefully at these two pictures. How many differences can you find?

19 Wordsearch

Look in the wordsearch grid for the six words listed below. You will find them by reading across or down. Circle the words.

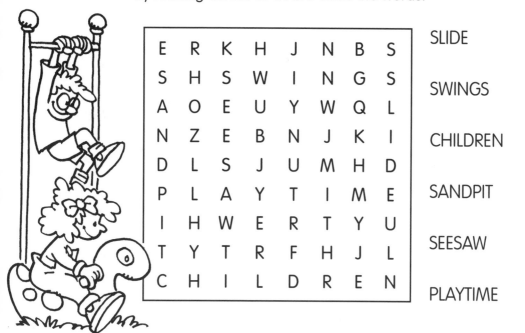

E	R	K	H	J	N	B	S
S	H	S	W	I	N	G	S
A	O	E	U	Y	W	Q	L
N	Z	E	B	N	J	K	I
D	L	S	J	U	M	H	D
P	L	A	Y	T	I	M	E
I	H	W	E	R	T	Y	U
T	Y	T	R	F	H	J	L
C	H	I	L	D	R	E	N

SLIDE

SWINGS

CHILDREN

SANDPIT

SEESAW

PLAYTIME

20 Math puzzle

Do the math in the grid by filling in the missing numbers.

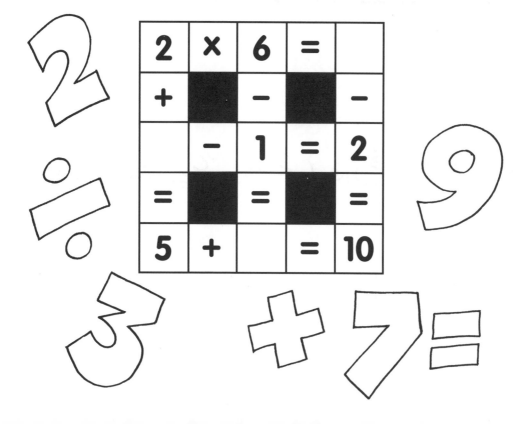

2	×	6	=	
+		−		−
	−	1	=	2
=		=		=
5	+		=	10

21 Ghostly goings on

Can you crack the code to work out what this ghost is saying?

tsoh gyld neir fama Ioll eh

_____

_____

_____

22 Which story?

Starting with the letter V cross out every other letter. You will end up with the name of a well-known fairy tale.

V S T L S E A E B P Q I R N L G

R B S E N A S U E T R Y

_____

_____

23 Trivia quiz

How many legs does a spider have?

a) 4

b) 6

c) 8

24 Puzzle wheel

Write the first letter of each picture in the space in the center of the puzzle wheel. You will spell a shape.

25 Hidden word

Cross out the letters that appear twice in the grid. The letters that are left spell a flower.

S	T	K	M	G
D	X	Q	U	O
B	L	N	X	D
K	O	G	I	S
N	Q	B	M	P

26 Words beginning with 'b'

Look carefully at this busy scene. How many words can you see that begin with 'b'?

27 Dot to dot

Starting with number 1, draw a line to join the dots and complete the picture.

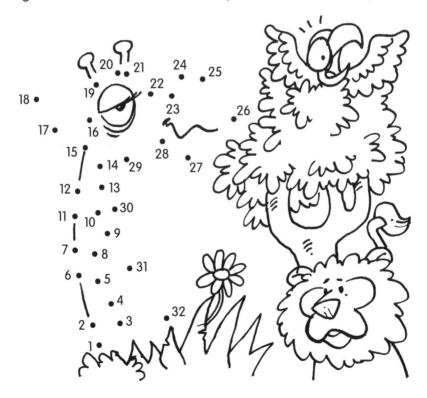

28 Words and meanings

All these words have another word that sounds the same but is spelt differently. Can you write the other words on the lines?

e.g. sun son

hare _____

pear _____

flower _____

29 Odd one out

Look carefully at this herd of elephants. Can you see an animal that doesn't belong?

30 **How many?**

How many new words can you make
from the word scarecrow?

S C A R E C R O W

31 **Math puzzle**

Do the math in the grid by filling in the missing numbers.

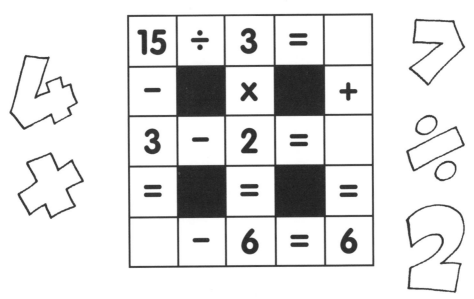

15	÷	3	=	
−		×		+
3	−	2	=	
=		=		=
	−	6	=	6

32 **Rhyming words**

How many more three letter words can you
think of that end with -at?

33 Reveal the picture

Shade in all the spaces marked with a dot to reveal the picture.

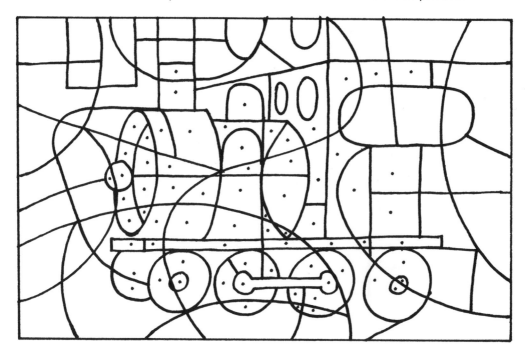

34 Coloring

Color this picture.

35 Maze

Help the helicopter through the maze to the helipad.

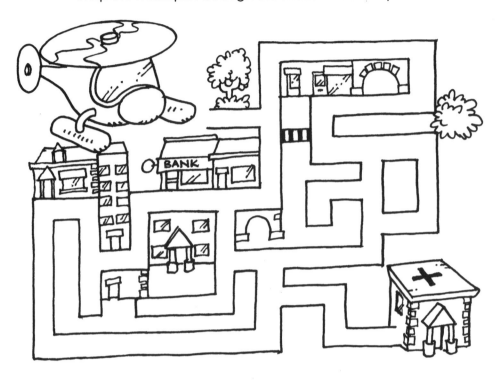

36 Complete the picture

Parts of this picture are missing. Draw over the dots to complete the picture.

37 Color by numbers

Color this picture by using the number key.
Then color the rest of the picture.

1 = green
2 = brown
3 = yellow

38 Number pattern

There is a pattern to this row of numbers. Can you write
in the missing numbers?

9, 18, ___, 36, ___, 54,

39 Puzzle wheel

Write the first letter of each picture in the space in the center of the puzzle wheel. Unscramble the letters and you will spell a baby animal.

40 Skyscraper

Which is the correct shadow to go with this building?

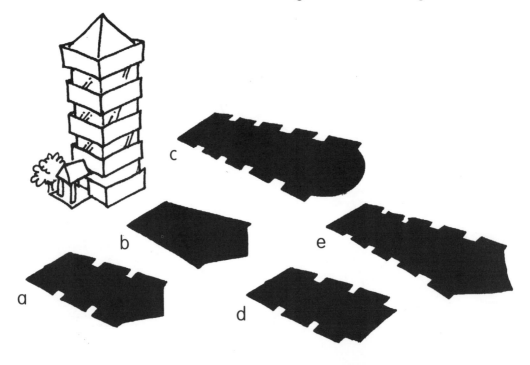

41 In the wrong place

Look at this underwater scene. There is an animal that doesn't belong.
Can you spot it?

42 Word trail

Use the picture clues to fill in the word trail – the last letter of each word is the first letter of the next.

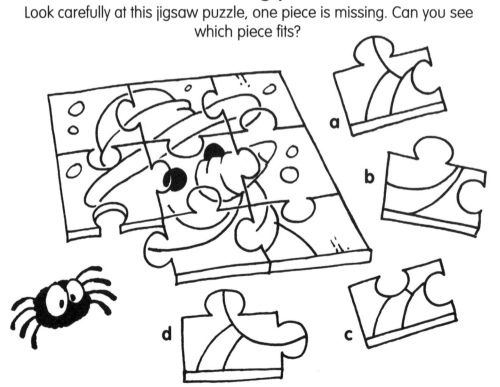

43 Missing piece

Look carefully at this jigsaw puzzle, one piece is missing. Can you see which piece fits?

44 Count the shapes

Look carefully at the playground scene. How many of these shapes can you count?

circle	
square	
triangle	
rectangle	

45 Who has what?

Follow the ribbons to see which Christmas present each child has. Can you tell what each gift is from its shape?

James   Susan   Simon

46 Mouse maze

Help the mouse get through the underground tunnels to the cup cakes.

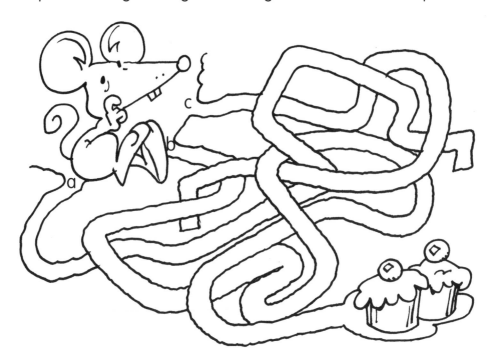

47 Dot to dot

Starting with number 1, draw a line to join the dots and complete the picture.

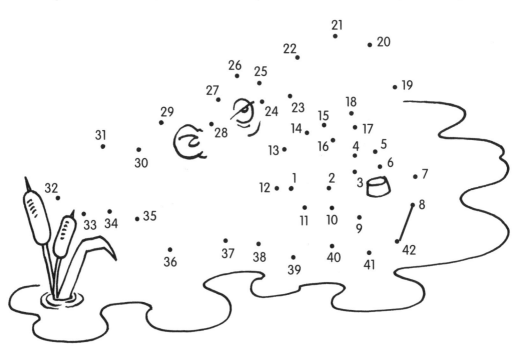

48 **Match the pair**

Draw a line to match two cakes.

a

b

c

d

e

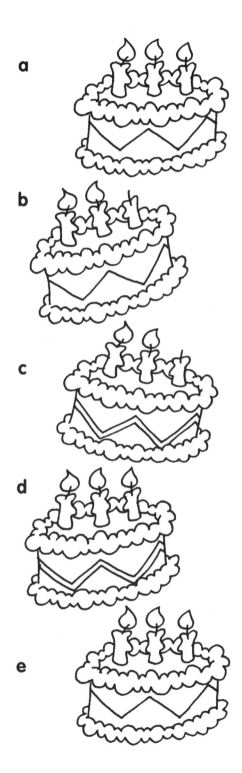

49 **Blowing bubbles**

How many bubbles has the boy blown? Write the answer on the line.

_____

50 **Spot the difference**

Look carefully at these two pictures. How many differences can you find?

51 **All around the world**

Unscramble the names of these places.

YEANK

_____

WONYAR

_____

PJANA

_____

52 On the farm

Look in the wordsearch grid for the names of six farm animals. You will find them by reading across or down. Circle the words.

W	E	R	T	Y	U	G	V
B	D	U	K	E	S	C	Z
G	O	A	T	T	F	O	H
V	G	S	A	W	E	W	F
V	X	C	D	O	P	U	Y
K	P	I	G	Y	T	R	E
E	R	E	W	H	D	G	F
O	S	H	E	E	P	Y	U
R	T	V	Y	N	K	I	H

53 Trivia quiz

Where is Uluru (formerly known as Ayers Rock)?

a) France
b) Brazil
c) Australia

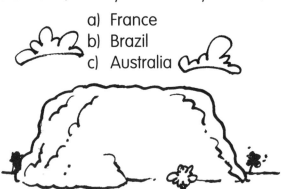

54 Hidden word

Cross out the letters that appear twice in the grid. The letters that are left will spell a creature you might find living near a pond.

F	A	P	I
S	Y	R	E
E	O	P	S
G	I	Y	A

55 How many?

How many new words can you make from the word helicopter?

HELICOPTER

56 Sporting fun!

The pictures of sports are clues. Follow the numbers across and down, and write the words in the grid.

57 Hidden toys

There are five different toys hidden in the garden, can you spot them?

58 Number pattern

There is a pattern to this row of numbers. Can you write in the missing numbers?

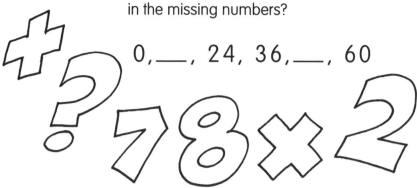

0, ___, 24, 36, ___, 60

59 Scrambled words

Can you unscramble these words? They are all things that you might find in a kitchen.

WEICRMOVA

_____

MWAASCHIHINENG

_____

AFEERRTROIGR

_____

DOCUBARP

_____

60 Mary had a little lamb

Finish the nursery rhyme by writing the missing words in the spaces.

Mary had a little _ _ _ _ _,

Its fleece was _ _ _ _ _ _ as snow;

And everywhere that Mary went

The lamb was sure to _ _.

61 Dot to dot

Starting with number 1, draw a line to join the dots and complete the picture.

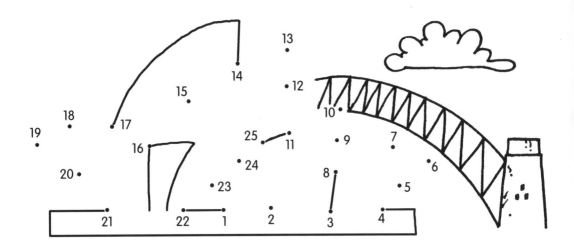

62 What am I?

I have six letters. I am a building.
My first is in cat but not in bat.
My second is in man but not in men.
My third is in sail but not in tail.
My fourth is in salt but not in sale.
My fifth is in low but not in cow.
My sixth is in sea but not in sat.

I am a

_____

63 At the beach

Look at this beach scene. Can you find someone wearing a striped t-shirt?

64 Puzzle wheel

Write the first letter of each picture in the space in the center of the puzzle wheel. Unscramble the letters and you will spell a fruit.

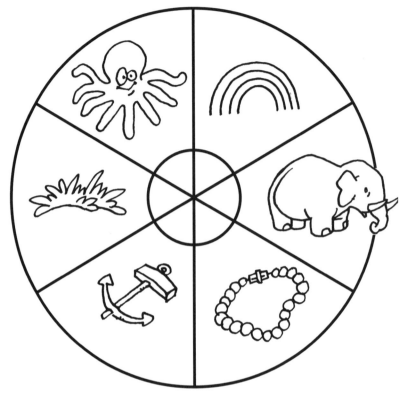

65 Dot to dot

Starting with number 1, draw a line to join the dots and complete the picture.

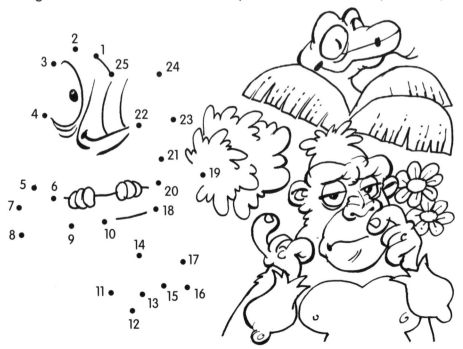

66 Word trail

Use the picture clues to fill in the word trail – the last letter of each word is the first letter of the next.

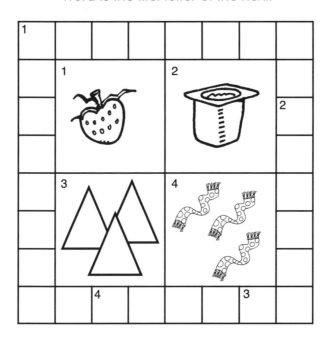

67 Little Boy Blue

Finish the nursery rhyme by writing the missing words in the spaces.

Little Boy _ _ _ _ come blow your horn,
The sheep is in the meadow,
the cow is in the _ _ _ _.
Where is the boy that looks
after the sheep?
He's under a haycock fast _ _ _ _ _ _ _.

68 Maze

Help the diver find his way through the underwater maze to the shipwreck.

69 Math puzzle

Do the math in the grid by filling in the missing numbers.

	−	16	=	3
+	■	−	■	+
2	+		=	14
=	■	=	■	=
21	−	4	=	

70 Hidden word

Cross out the letters that appear twice in the grid. The letters that are left spell an item of clothing.

O	H	M	L	I
I	Y	S	B	R
D	A	R	O	C
N	M	D	Y	S
T	C	L	B	N

71 How many?

How many new words can you make from the word caterpillar?

CATERPILLAR

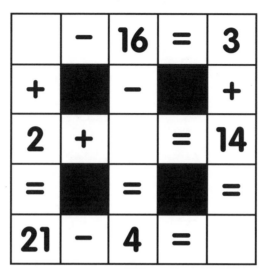

72 Coloring
Color this picture.

73 Reveal the picture
Shade in all the spaces marked with a dot to reveal the picture.

74 Wordsearch

Look in the wordsearch grid for the eight words listed below. You will find them by reading across or down. Circle the words.

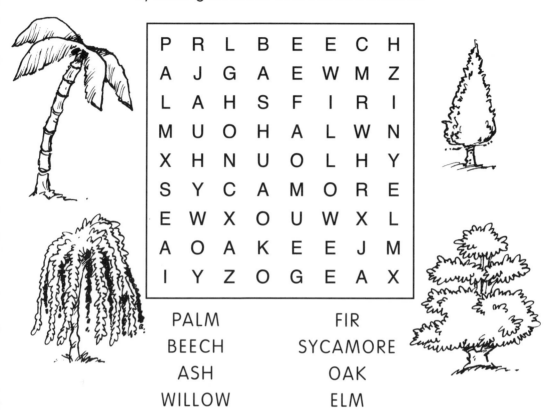

P	R	L	B	E	E	C	H
A	J	G	A	E	W	M	Z
L	A	H	S	F	I	R	I
M	U	O	H	A	L	W	N
X	H	N	U	O	L	H	Y
S	Y	C	A	M	O	R	E
E	W	X	O	U	W	X	L
A	O	A	K	E	E	J	M
I	Y	Z	O	G	E	A	X

PALM   FIR
BEECH   SYCAMORE
ASH   OAK
WILLOW   ELM

75 Word trail

Use the picture clues to fill in the word trail – the last letter of each word is the first letter of the next.

76 Trivia quiz
A diplodocus was a type of what?

a) transport
b) dinosaur
c) bird

77 Hat trick
Draw lines to match people with their hats.

78 Silhouettes

Look carefully at the silhouettes, write
what they are on the lines below.

_____

_____

_____

79 Scrambled words

Can you unscramble these words?
They are all things that go.

ROECFHVRAT

_____

PLNRAEAI

_____

INGCRA RAC

_____

CTTRAOR

_____

80 Maze

Help the go-cart through the maze to the finish line.

FINISH

81 Number code

Can you work out what each number symbol represents by doing the math?

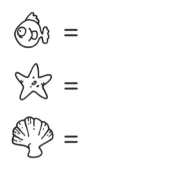

$$\text{fish} \times \text{fish} = 9$$

$$\text{shell} + 2 = 9$$

$$10 - \text{star} = \text{star}$$

82 Dot to dot

Starting with number 1, draw a line to join the dots and complete the picture.

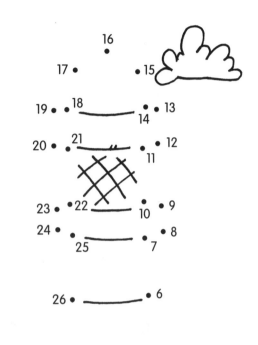

83 Scrambled words

Can you unscramble these words? They are all things that you might find in the ocean.

SPOUTOC

_____

RSHAFTIS

_____

STEOBLR

_____

BACR

_____

84 I had a little nut tree

Finish the nursery rhyme by writing
the missing words in the spaces.

I had a little nut _ _ _ _ _,

Nothing would it bear

But a _ _ _ _ _ _ _ nutmeg

And a golden _ _ _ _.

85 Match the pairs

Draw lines to join the matching pairs of candy.
Which one is the odd one out?

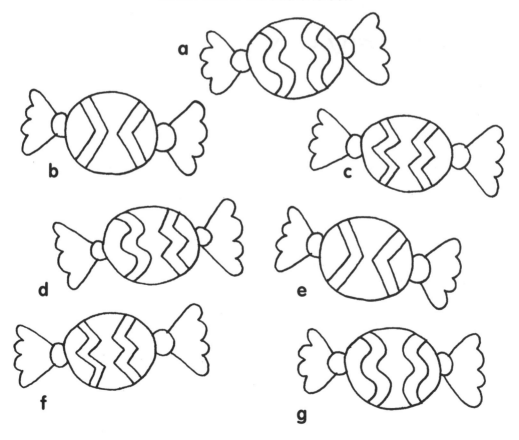

a

b

c

d

e

f

g

86 **Soccer fun**

Look carefully at this crowd of soccer fans. Can you find the polka-dotted hat?

87 Puzzle wheel

Write the first letter of each picture in the space in the center of the
puzzle wheel. You will spell a boy's name.

88 Magic math

Follow the steps below to see what answer you get.
Try the math again but start with a different number each time.

Think of a number ☐ – 4 =

× 5 =

+ 10 =

÷ 5 =

+ 7 =

– (minus the number
you first though of)

= ☐

89 **Match the pair**

Draw a line to join the matching backpacks.

90 **Jigsaw pieces**

Draw lines to connect the jigsaw pieces that go together to make three pictures of vegetables.

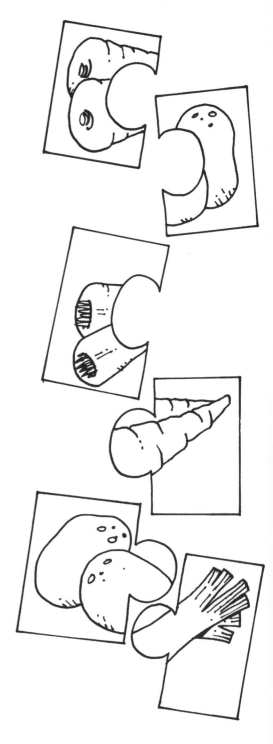

91 Spot the difference

Look carefully at these two pictures. How many differences can you find?

92 Wordsearch

How many times can you find the word flower in the wordsearch grid?
Circle the word each time you find it.

Z	F	F	L	O	W	E	R
F	L	O	W	E	R	F	N
E	O	A	F	B	X	L	R
X	W	K	L	I	F	O	P
F	E	V	O	O	L	W	R
M	R	D	W	N	O	E	X
F	L	K	E	D	W	R	C
B	Y	Z	E	M	E	X	Y
F	L	O	W	E	R	S	D

93 Math puzzle

Do the math in the grid by filling in the missing numbers.

3	**+**		**=**	**12**
×		**×**		**÷**
	÷	**2**	**=**	**6**
=		**=**		**=**
36	**÷**		**=**	**2**

94 Count the crowns

How many crown shapes can you count?

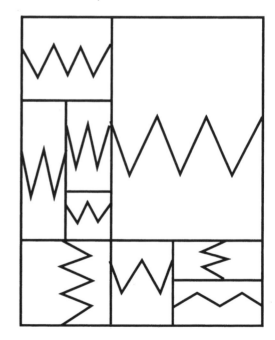

95 Where in the world?

Unscramble the letters to spell the name of a famous landmark.

TUASET
FO RYBTIEL

_____

96 Times square

Do the multiplication and write the numbers in the grid, following the examples.

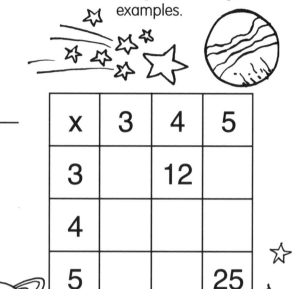

x	3	4	5
3		12	
4			
5			25

97 Puzzle wheel

Write the first letter of each picture in the space in the center of the puzzle wheel. Unscramble the letters and you will spell a girl's name.

98 Hidden word

Cross out the letters that appear twice in the grid. The letters that are left spell an animal.

T	W	A	I
N	P	D	O
L	I	T	P
A	D	F	N

99 Words beginning with 'L'

Look carefully at this busy scene. How many words can you see that begin with 'L'?

100 Dot to dot

Starting with number 1, draw a line to join the dots and complete the picture.

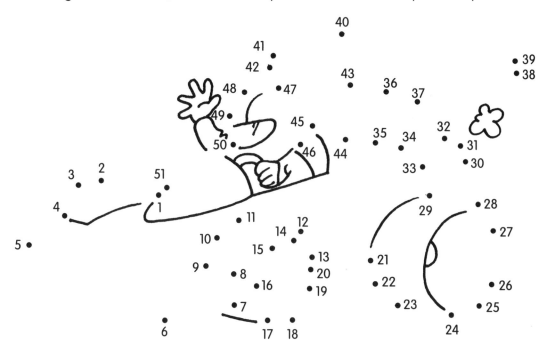

101 Rhyming words

How many more three letter words can you think of that end with -en?

Color this picture.

103 Home from home

Draw lines to match the dogs with their kennels.

104 Mmm...maze

Help the boy through the maze to the ice-cream sundaes.

105 Color by numbers

Color this picture by using the number key. Then color the rest of the picture.

1 = purple
2 = blue
3 = red
4 = green

106 Reveal the picture

Shade in all the spaces marked with a dot to reveal the picture.

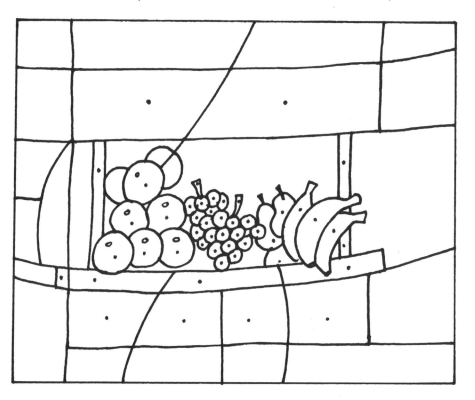

107 Dot to dot

Starting with number 1, draw a line to join the dots and complete the picture.

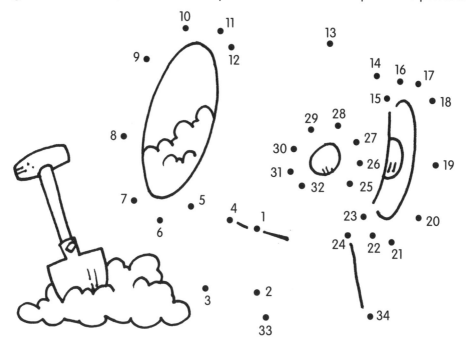

108 Shadows

Draw a line from the picture to its shadow.

109 Copy and draw

Use the grid to help you draw the other half of the hot air balloon,
copying square by square.

110 Rhyming words

How many more three letter words can you think of that end with -ot?

111 **Number codes**

There is a pattern to the rows of numbers. Write in the missing numbers.

a 2, ___, 6, 8, ___, 12

b 5, 10, ___, ___, 25

c 4, 8, 12, ___, ___

113 **Signs**

Unscramble the names of these cities.

112 **Puzzle wheel**

Write the first letter of each picture in the space in the center of the puzzle wheel. Unscramble the letters and you will spell a tropical bird.

PEMMISH

COSTUN

WEN KROY

SLALAD

114 In the wrong place

Look at this shoal of fish. There is an animal that doesn't belong, can you spot it?

115 Count the shapes

How many of these shapes can you count in the picture?

□ squares	
○ circles	
△ triangles	

116 Missing piece

Look carefully at this jigsaw puzzle, one piece is missing. Can you see which is the correct one?

117 Who will win the race?

Add up the number of minutes to see who will win the race. Each symbol represents a different number of minutes.

118 Maze

Help the butterfly through the maze
to the flowers.

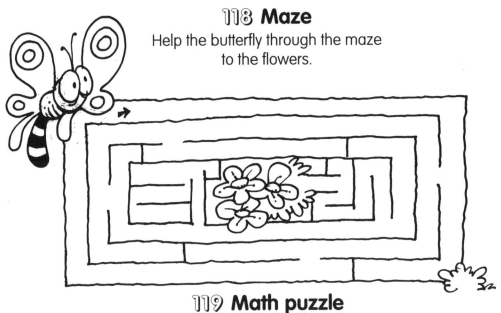

119 Math puzzle

Do the math in the grid by filling in the missing numbers.

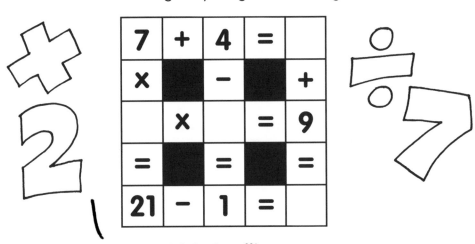

7	+	4	=	
×		−		+
	×		=	9
=		=		=
21	−	1	=	

120 Spelling

Some of these months of the year have letters missing.
Can you fill in the missing letters?

_ A _ U _ R _

N _ _ E M _ _ R

F _ _ R _ A _ Y

_ _ R C H

121 Traveling companions

There are some small creatures hidden in this picture. How many can you see?

122 Color by numbers

Color this picture by using the number key. Then color
the rest of the picture.

1 = red
2 = yellow
3 = blue
4 = green

123 Copy and draw

Use the grid to help you draw this giraffe, copying square by square.

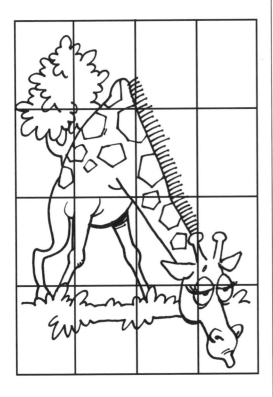

124 Wordsearch

Look in the wordsearch grid for the names of six planets. You will find them by reading across or down. Circle the words.

E	W	Q	T	P	R	Y	U
Z	X	C	V	L	B	N	M
M	E	R	C	U	R	Y	A
E	A	W	D	T	F	A	R
B	R	A	E	O	I	O	S
C	T	S	A	T	U	R	N
V	H	Q	S	G	V	M	A
L	P	N	O	O	T	S	R
U	T	A	V	E	N	U	S

125 Word trail

Use the picture clues to fill in the word trail – the last letter of each word is the first letter of the next.

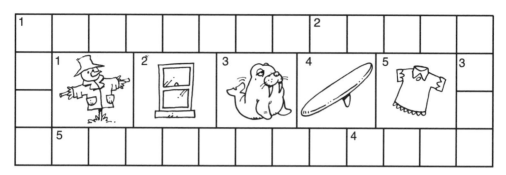

126 Dot to dot

Starting with number 1, draw a line to join the dots and complete the picture.

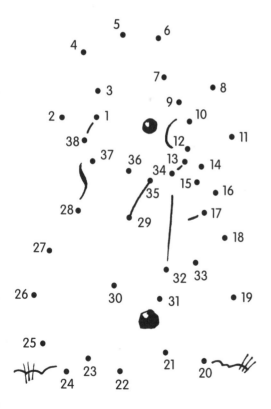

127 Trivia quiz

Where do carrots grow?

a) in a carrot tree
b) underground
c) underwater

128 **Going home**
Follow the lines to see which car is going to the house.

129 **Scrambled words**
Can you unscramble these words? They are all things that you might find at school.

DITOCAINRY

_____

ECEHATR

_____

NIECPL ASEC

_____

130 Silhouettes

Look carefully at the silhouettes, write what they are on the lines below.

_____

_____

_____

131 Match the pair

Draw a line to join the matching pair of socks.

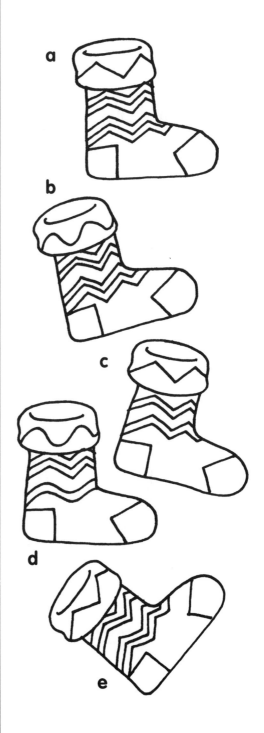

132 Jigsaw pieces

Draw lines to connect the jigsaw pieces that go together
to make three pictures of flowers.

133 Spot the difference

Look carefully at these two pictures. How many differences can you find?

Color this picture.

135 Math puzzle

Do the math in the grid by filling in the missing numbers.

12	+	3	=	
−	■	×	■	÷
	−		=	5
=	■	=	■	=
6	−		=	3

136 Break the code

Can you work out what the message says
that the spy has left for his boss?

ME ETMEB YTH
ECLOCK

_____

137 Where in the world?

Starting with the letter A cross out every other letter. You will end up with
the name of a famous place.

A G D R K A S N T D

_____

V C P A L N E Y U O Q N

_____

138 Trivia quiz

How many weeks are there in a year?

a) 48
b) 52
c) 54

139 Puzzle wheel

Write the first letter of each picture in the space in the center of the puzzle wheel. Unscramble the letters and you will spell a continent.

140 Hidden word

Cross out the letters that appear twice in the grid. The letters that are left spell a girl's name.

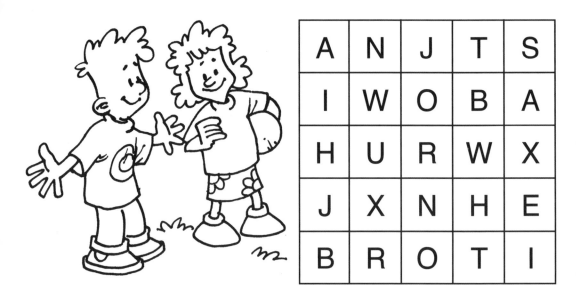

A	N	J	T	S
I	W	O	B	A
H	U	R	W	X
J	X	N	H	E
B	R	O	T	I

141 Copy and draw

Use the grid to help you draw the other half of the robot, copying square by square.

142 Dot to dot

Starting with number 1, draw a line to join the dots and complete the picture.

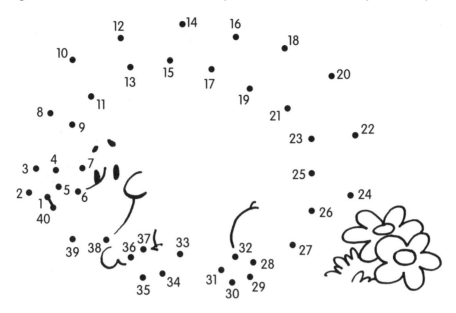

143 Maze

Help the children through the maze to the swing.

144 **Odd one out**

Look carefully at the swarm of bees. Can you see a creature that doesn't belong?

145 **How many?**

How many new words can you make from the word snowman?

SNOWMAN

146 Coloring
Color this picture.

147 Words beginning with 's'
Look carefully at this busy scene. How many words can you see
that begin with 's'?

148 Reveal the picture

Shade in all the spaces marked with a dot to reveal the picture.

149 Missing piece

Look carefully at this jigsaw puzzle, one piece is missing.
Can you see which one fits?

150 Tell the time

The hands are missing from the clocks and the watch. Read the different times
and work out where to draw the hands.

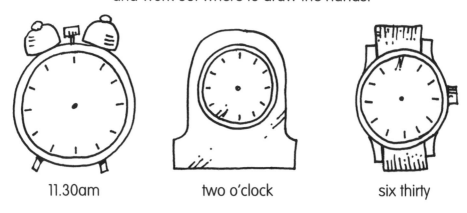

11.30am   two o'clock   six thirty

151 Complete the picture

Parts of this picture are missing. Draw over the dots to complete the picture.

152 Color by numbers

Color this picture by using the number key. Then color the rest of the picture.

1 = purple
2 = pink
3 = green
4 = blue
5 = red

153 Number codes

Using the code in the box as a guide, fill in the missing numbers
and draw the missing pictures.

1		2		3		4		5	
6		7		8		9		10	

8   2   6

154 Counting

How many birds, flowers, and bees can you count?

birds	flowers	bees

155 **Crazy car**

Which is the correct shadow to go with this car?

156 **Odd one out**

Look carefully at the jungle scene. Can you see a creature that doesn't belong?

157 Word trail

Use the picture clues to fill in the word trail – the last letter of each word is the first letter of the next.

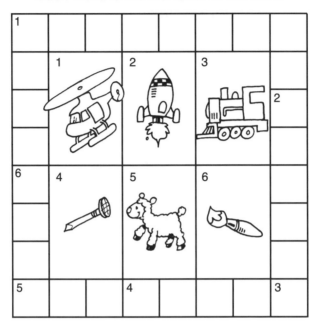

158 Missing piece

Look carefully at this jigsaw puzzle, one piece is missing. Can you see which piece fits?

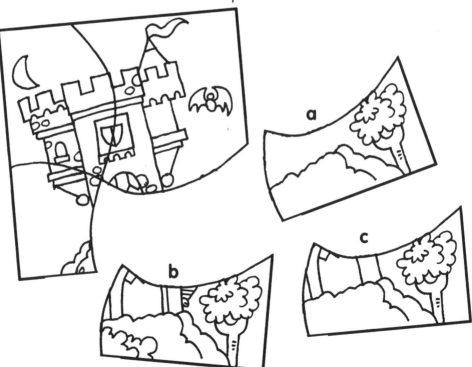

159 Count the shapes

Look carefully at the busy scene, how many of these shapes can you count?

☐ squares	
◯ circles	
△ triangles	

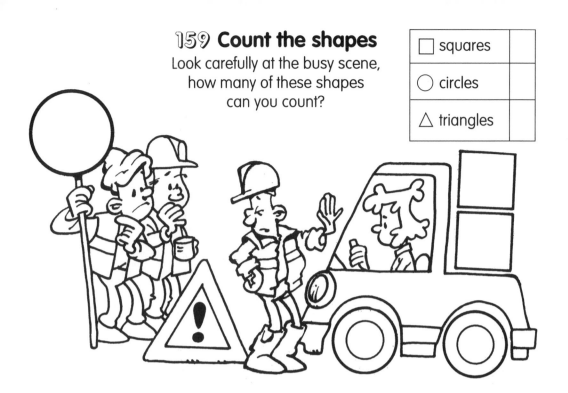

160 Bon voyage!

Follow the lines to see what kind of vacation each person is going on.

161 Maze

Help the boy through the maze to the beach.

162 Dot to dot

Starting with number 1, draw a line to join the dots and complete the picture.

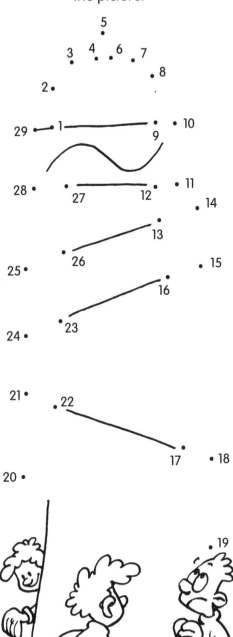

163 Match the pair

Draw a line to join the matching fish.

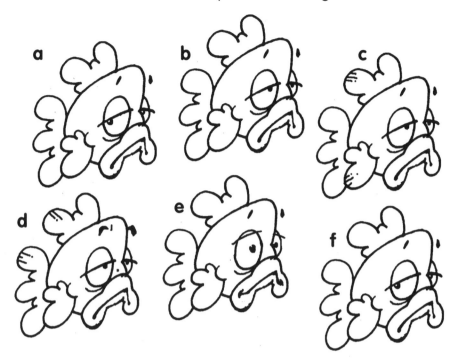

a   b   c

d   e   f

164 Buttoned up!

How many buttons can you count?

165 Spot the difference

Look carefully at these two pictures. How many differences can you find?

166 Climb every mountain

Can you unscramble these words? They are the names of mountain ranges.

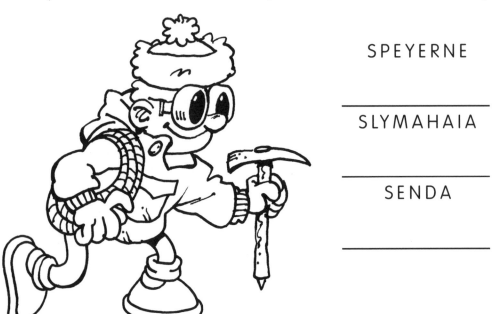

SPEYERNE

_____

SLYMAHAIA

_____

SENDA

_____

167 Wordsearch

Look in the wordsearch grid for the names of seven flowers. You will find them by reading across or down. Circle the words.

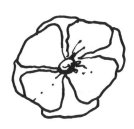

D	A	S	D	F	G	Y	O
A	Q	E	T	U	L	I	P
I	P	G	R	F	X	R	M
S	D	T	D	X	O	I	W
Y	P	N	M	R	F	S	A
D	A	F	F	O	D	I	L
S	N	G	X	S	P	O	Q
O	S	E	B	E	Z	Y	N
I	Y	K	P	O	P	P	Y

168 Trivia quiz

How many sides does a hexagon have?

a) 4
b) 6
c) 8

169 Hidden word

Cross out the letters that appear twice in the grid. The letters that are left spell a part of the body.

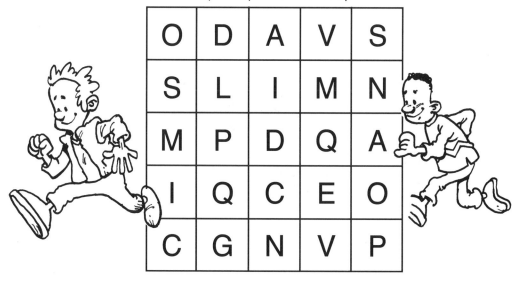

O	D	A	V	S
S	L	I	M	N
M	P	D	Q	A
I	Q	C	E	O
C	G	N	V	P

170 Which symbols?

Write the missing math symbols in the boxes.

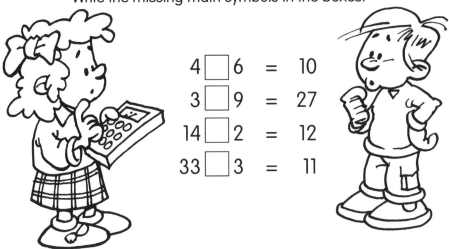

$$4 \; \square \; 6 = 10$$
$$3 \; \square \; 9 = 27$$
$$14 \; \square \; 2 = 12$$
$$33 \; \square \; 3 = 11$$

171 Caterpillar math

Follow the instructions on each caterpillar carefully and do the math.
Write your answers in the boxes.

$$2 \; \underset{8}{+} \; \underset{2}{\times} \; \underset{4}{\div} \; = \; \square$$

$$3 \; \underset{3}{\times} \; \underset{6}{+} \; \underset{5}{\div} \; = \; \square$$

172 Which is the tallest?

Which sunflower do you think has the longest stem?

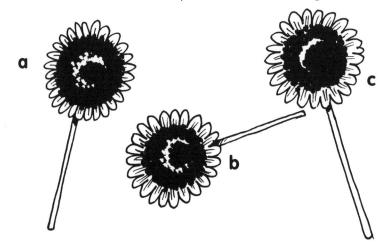

a

b

c

173 Hidden mouse

Can you find the hidden mouse in this woodland scene?

174 Scrambled words

Can you unscramble these words? They are all birds.

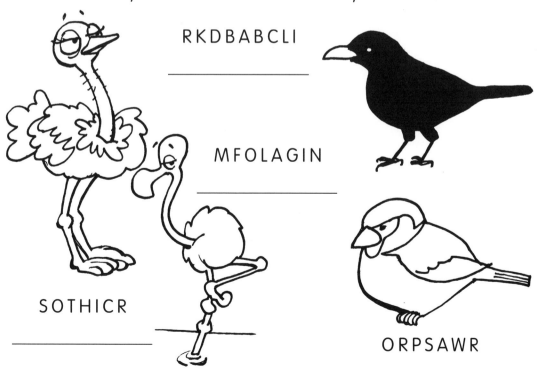

RKDBABCLI

_____

MFOLAGIN

_____

SOTHICR

_____

ORPSAWR

_____

175 Spot the difference

Look carefully at these two pictures. How many differences can you find?

176 Dot to dot

Starting with number 1, draw a line to join the dots and complete the picture.

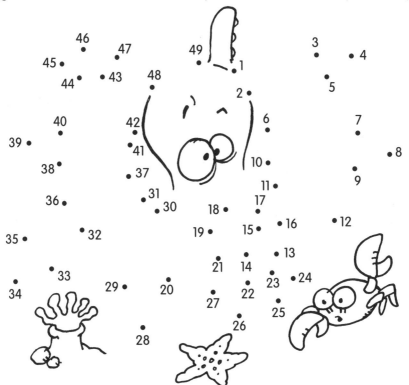

177 What am I?

I have five letters
My first is in sat but not in say
My second is in till but not in tall
My third is in got but not in hot
My fourth is in men but not in man
My fifth is in rail but not in sail.

I am a

_____

178 Fun at the pool

Look at this swimming pool scene. Can you find a toy duck?

179 **Copy and draw**

Use the grid to help you draw this
zebra, copying square by square.

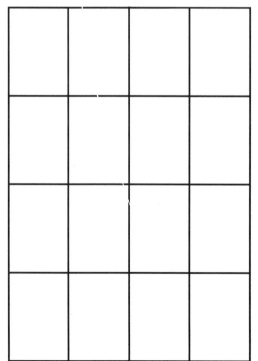

180 **Reveal the picture**

Shade in all the spaces marked with
a dot to reveal the picture.

181 Spelling

These words are spelt incorrectly.
Write the correct spelling on the line.

MONKY

GIRAFE   ZEEBRA

LEPARD

182 Creepie crawlie crossword

The pictures of creepy crawlies are clues. Follow the numbers across and down, and write the words in the grid.

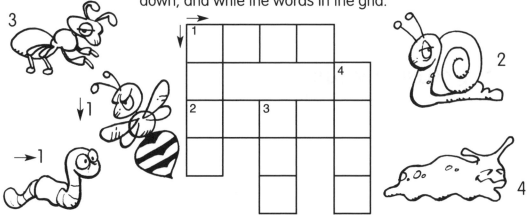

183 Odd one out

Look carefully at these animals. Can you see who doesn't belong?

184 Counting

The candy and marbles are mixed up. How many pieces of candy can you count, and how many marbles? Write your answers in the boxes.

candy = [ ]

marbles = [ ]

185 Hidden word

Cross out the letters that appear twice in the grid. The letters that are left spell a boy's name.

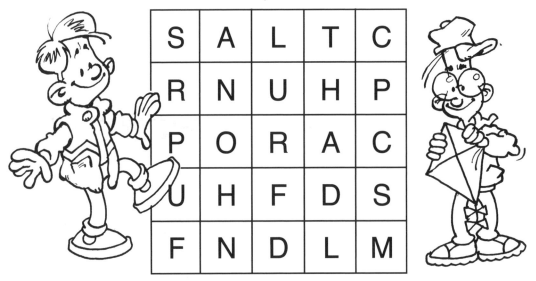

S	A	L	T	C
R	N	U	H	P
P	O	R	A	C
U	H	F	D	S
F	N	D	L	M

186 Trivia quiz

Is the Tasmanian devil a real animal or a made-up one?

187 Spot the difference

Look carefully at these two pictures.
How many differences can you find?

188 What am I?

I have six letters.
I am a type of mythical creature.
My first is in dawn but not in yawn
My second is in grow but not in glow
My third is in sand but not in send
My fourth is in tiger but not in timer
My fifth is in toil but not in tail
My sixth is in nest but not in test

I am a

_____

189 Crossword

The pictures of animals are clues. Follow the numbers across and down, and write the words in the grid.

190 Spelling

These words are spelt wrongly, write the correct spelling on the line.

KESTRL

_____

VULTRE

_____

EAGEL

_____

TAWNEY OWL

_____

191 Missing piece

Look carefully at this jigsaw puzzle, one piece is missing.
Can you see which piece fits?

192 Who has what?

Follow the lines to see which child will be doing each activity.

193 Shadows

Which is the correct shadow to go with this boy?

194 Reveal the picture

Shade in all the spaces marked with a dot to reveal the picture.

195 **Maze**

Help the fish through the maze to its friends.

196 **Rhyming words**

How many more four letter words can you find that end with -ent?

197 A bit fishy!
Look at this underwater scene. How many fish can you count?

198 Triangles
How many triangles can you count?

199 What toy?

Starting with the letter P cross out every other letter. You will spell the name of a toy.

P J L A Y C M K W I R N Q
T M H D E N B R O S X

_____

200 Hidden word

Cross out the letters that appear twice in the grid. The letters that are left spell something you find at the beach.

P	E	T	S
M	A	R	P
R	W	M	N
E	D	W	T

201 What am I?

I have five letters. I am a type of bird.
My first is in heir but not hair
My second is in sand but not in send
My third is gasp but not in wasp
My fourth is in less but not in mess
My fifth is in east but not in cast.

I am an

_____

202 **Puzzle wheel**

Write the first letter of each picture in the space in the center of the puzzle wheel. You will spell a new word.

203 **Copy and draw**

Use the grid to help you draw the other half of this girl, copying square by square.

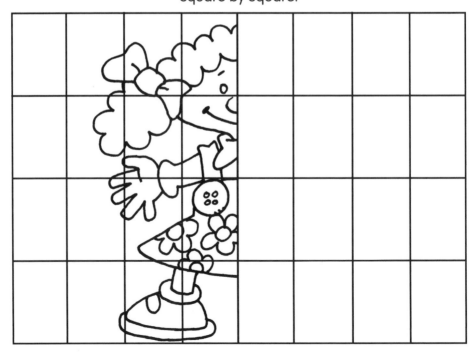

204 At school

Look at this school room scene. How many pens can you count?

205 Flower math

Look at the numbers in the flowers and do the math.

17 + 13 =

206 Trivia quiz

Which is the capital city of Australia?

a) Canberra
b) Perth
c) Sydney

207 Reveal the picture

Shade in all the spaces marked with a dot to reveal the picture.

208 Hidden word

Cross out the letters that appear twice in the grid.
The letters that are left spell a vegetable.

S	T	Y	P	O
W	H	R	G	S
Y	E	L	O	W
N	G	N	C	R
A	C	T	H	L

209 Counting

How many fish are there in the pond?

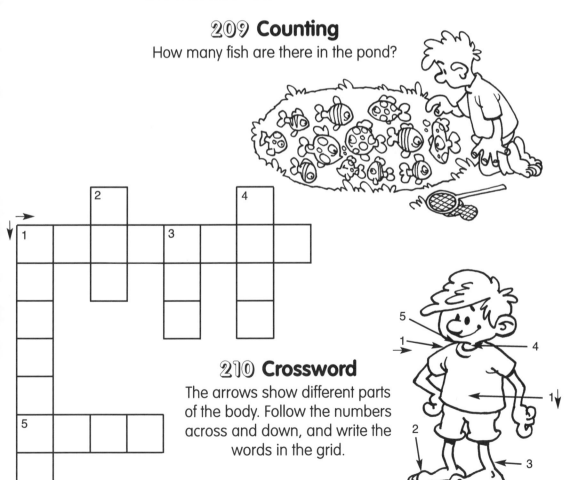

210 Crossword

The arrows show different parts
of the body. Follow the numbers
across and down, and write the
words in the grid.

211 Jigsaw pieces

These jigsaw pieces are jumbled up. Can you tell which piece will **not** fit the puzzle?

212 Match the pair

Draw a line to join the matching cats.

213 Tangled giraffes

These three giraffes have got into a tangle. Can you work out which head goes with which body?

214 Odd one out

Look carefully at the pictures. Can you spot the one that does not belong?

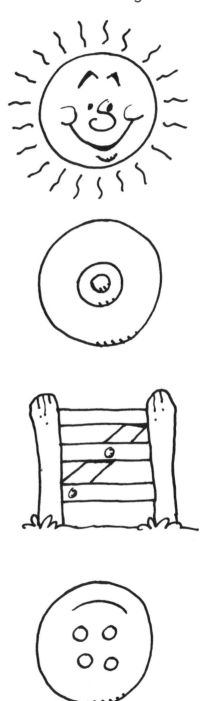

215 What am I?

I have four letters. I am something you find everywhere.
My first is in rail but not in tail
My second is in fog but not in fig
My third is in meat but not in meet
My fourth is in deal but not in meal.

I am a

_____

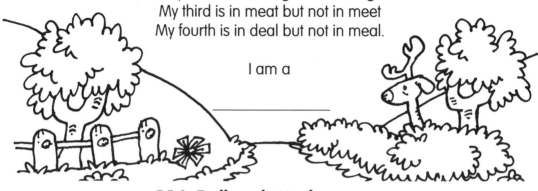

216 Polka-dotted scarves

Look carefully at these scarves. Which has the most polka-dots?

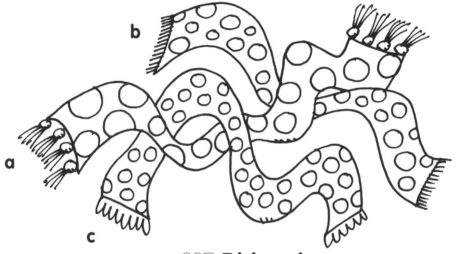

217 Trivia quiz

Which is the eleventh month of the year?

a) December
b) October
c) November

218 Maze

How quickly can you get the skier to the finish post?

219 Copy and draw

Use the grid to help you draw this helicopter, copying square by square.

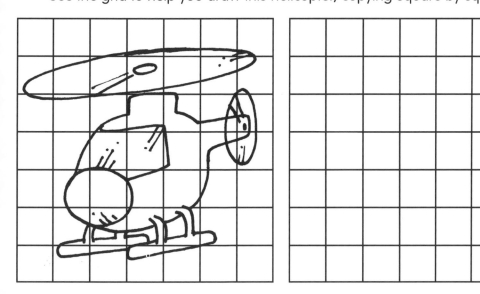

220 Who has won?

Follow the lines to see who has won the cup.

a

b

c

221 Scrambled animals

Unscramble the names of these
strange animals.

MADLOARIL

_____

AGONR-TNAU

_____

ZEGALEL

_____

CONURPIPE

_____

222 Dot to dot

Starting with number 1, join the dots and complete the picture.

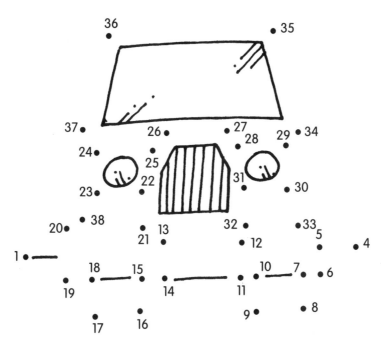

223 Match the pairs

Draw lines to join the matching pairs of houses.
Which is the odd one?

224 Words beginning with 'd'

Look carefully at this busy scene. How many words can you see that begin with 'd'?

225 Spot the difference

Look carefully at these two pictures. How many differences can you find?

226 Crossword

The pictures of clothes are clues. Follow the numbers across and down, and write the words in the grid.

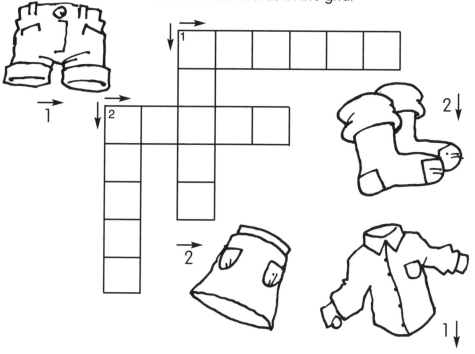

227 Math puzzle

Do the math in the grid by filling in the missing numbers.

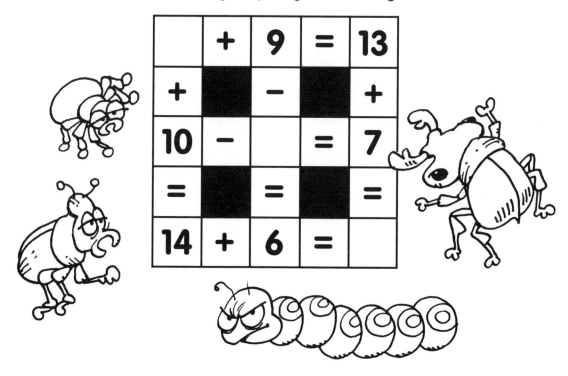

228 Copy and draw

Use the grid to help you draw the other half of the scarecrow, copying square by square.

229 What is it?

Starting with the letter B cross out every other letter. You will end up with something you see in the sky.

B R P A W I F N Q B L O R W

230 Mystery word

Find the right letters in the grid to fill in the blanks and you will spell a country.

___ ___ ___ ___ ___ ___ ___
A3   C4   D4   F2   C1   B6   E2

	1	2	3	4	5	6
A	C	M	H	S	K	M
B	S	W	R	S	A	N
C	A	B	A	O	M	Q
D	X	H	L	L	T	A
E	P	D	E	Y	T	H
F	T	L	T	I	M	H

231 Reveal the picture

Shade in all the spaces marked with a dot to reveal the picture.

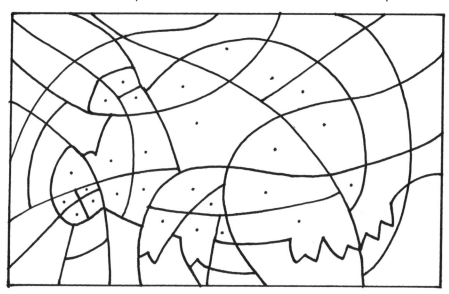

232 Hidden flowers

There are some flowers hidden in this bedroom scene, can you spot them?

233 Scrambled words

Unscramble the names of these planets.

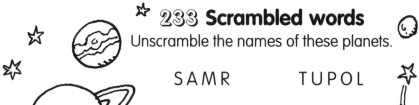

SAMR _____

TUPOL _____

NEVSU _____

YERRUCM _____

234 Wordsearch

Look in the wordsearch grid for the names of these animals. You will find them by reading across or down. Circle the words.

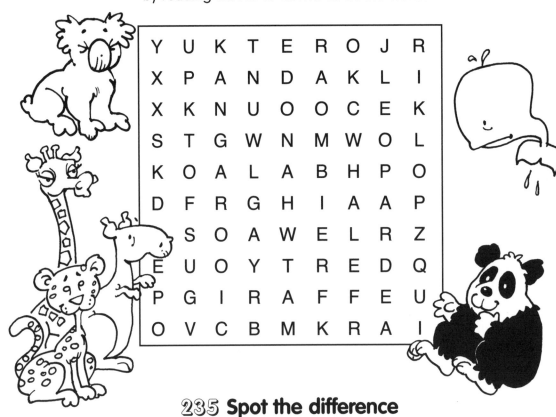

Y	U	K	T	E	R	O	J	R
X	P	A	N	D	A	K	L	I
X	K	N	U	O	O	C	E	K
S	T	G	W	N	M	W	O	L
K	O	A	L	A	B	H	P	O
D	F	R	G	H	I	A	A	P
S	O	A	W	E	L	R	Z	
E	U	O	Y	T	R	E	D	Q
P	G	I	R	A	F	F	E	U
O	V	C	B	M	K	R	A	I

235 Spot the difference

Look carefully at these two pictures. How many differences can you find?

236 Match the pair

Draw a line to join the matching pair of frogs.

237 Which is shortest?

Look carefully at the candy jars in the shop window. Which is the shortest?

238 Going batty!
Count Dracula has lost count of the bats. Can you count them for him?

239 Signs
Unscramble the names of these cities.

PAMAT

SLUMBUCO

TEASLET

240 Heads and feet

Draw lines to match the hats with the footwear.

241 Coloring

Color this picture.

242 Maze

Help the lamb through the maze to the other sheep.

243 Complete the picture

Draw over the dotted lines to complete the picture.

244 Hidden word

Cross out the letters that appear twice in the grid.
The letters that are left spell a type of vehicle.

R	V	E	Y	S
P	U	M	L	R
S	E	A	Q	L
B	D	U	D	P
N	Q	M	Y	B

245 Trivia quiz

How many years are there in a century?

a) 10
b) 100
c) 1000

246 Puzzle wheel

Write the first letter of each picture in the space in the center of the puzzle wheel. You will spell the name of a planet.

247 Hidden treasure

There are some pieces of treasure hidden on this desert island. Can you spot them?

248 Mirror image
Which do you think is the dog's true reflection?

a

b

c

249 How many?
How many new words can you make from the word wheelbarrow?

WHEELBARROW

250 **Missing piece**

Look carefully at this jigsaw puzzle, one piece is missing.
Can you see which one fits?

a

b

c

251 **Count the shapes**

How many squares, circles, and rectangles can you count?

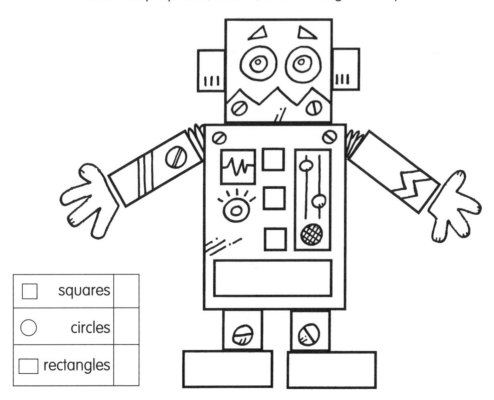

	squares	
◯	circles	
▭	rectangles	

252 Feathered friends

The pictures of birds are clues. Follow the numbers across and down, and write the words in the grid.

253 Maze

Help the tourist through the streets to the statue.

254 Dot to dot

Starting with number 1, join the dots and complete the picture.

255 Match the pairs

Draw lines to join the matching pairs of butterflies.

a

b

c

d

e

f

256 Fall leaves

Look at this fall scene. How many leaves can you count?

257 We're hungry!

Draw lines to connect each animal with its favorite food.

258 **Letter change**

Fill in the missing letters to change the
word HEAD into the word FOOT.

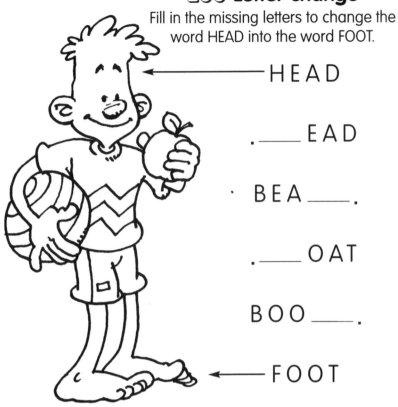

H E A D

.___E A D

· B E A___.

.___O A T

B O O___.

F O O T

259 **Wordsearch**

Look in the wordsearch grid for the names of these fruits. You will find them
by reading across or down. Draw a ring around the words.

Q	W	L	E	M	O	N	V	X
R	E	B	C	X	Z	M	P	P
T	Y	A	P	P	L	E	L	K
U	I	N	D	F	G	L	H	J
O	R	A	N	G	E	O	G	X
O	P	N	S	A	P	N	R	L
A	S	A	T	Y	U	I	A	O
D	F	G	R	E	E	W	P	Q
H	P	E	A	R	M	K	E	N
J	K	L	Z	X	C	V	S	B

260 Coloring
Color this picture.

261 Dot to dot
Starting with number 1, join the dots and complete the picture.

262 What am I?

I have five letters
My first is in hat but not in bat
My second is in mop but not in map
My third is in nut but not in net
My fourth is in test but not in tent
My fifth is in tale but not in tall

I am a

_____

263 Funny footprints

Draw lines to connect the footprints with their owners.

264 Hidden word

Cross out the letters that appear twice in the grid. The letters that are left spell the name of a planet.

M	D	U	K
O	E	I	A
U	R	D	K
I	E	O	S

265 Spot the difference

Look carefully at these two pictures. How many differences can you find?

266 Word jumble

Two words have been jumbled together on this line, can you work out what they are?

ELBMOTICOYCRCLYEC

_____ _____

267 Letter wheel

Starting with the letter s, write every other letter on the lines until you have gone clockwise around the wheel twice. Find out where the family are going.

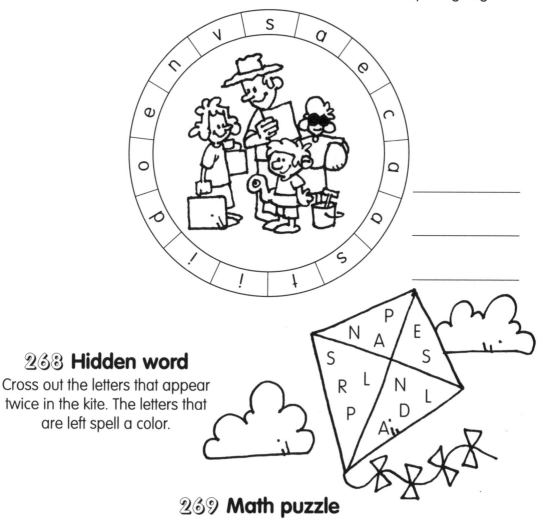

_____

_____

_____

268 Hidden word

Cross out the letters that appear twice in the kite. The letters that are left spell a color.

269 Math puzzle

Do the math in the grid by filling in the missing numbers.

12	+	4	=	
-	■	+	■	-
10	-		=	8
=	■	=	■	=
2	+	6	=	

270 Triangle?

There are ten patterned balls making a triangle shape. Move only three balls to make the triangle go the other way up.

271 Caterpillar math

Count the caterpillars and do the math. Write your answer in the box.

272 Pretty petals

Look carefully at the daisy and count how many petals there are. Write your answer in the center.

273 Reveal the picture

Shade in all the spaces marked with a dot to reveal the picture.

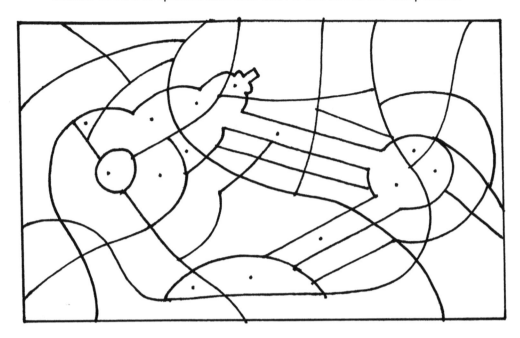

274 Wordsearch

Look in the wordsearch grid for things you will find on a construction site. You will find them by reading across or down. Circle the words.

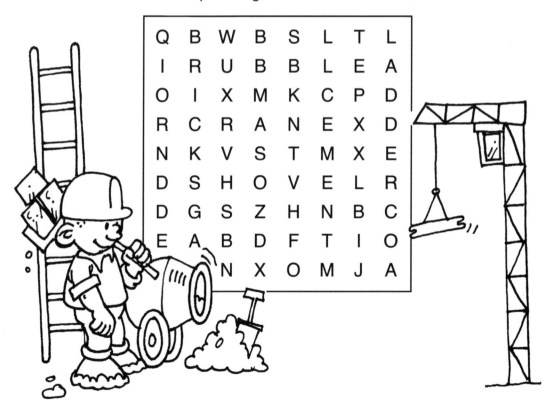

Q	B	W	B	S	L	T	L
I	R	U	B	B	L	E	A
O	I	X	M	K	C	P	D
R	C	R	A	N	E	X	D
N	K	V	S	T	M	X	E
D	S	H	O	V	E	L	R
D	G	S	Z	H	N	B	C
E	A	B	D	F	T	I	O
N	X	O	M	J	A		

275 **Word trail**

Use the picture clues to fill in the word trail – the last letter of each word is the first letter of the next.

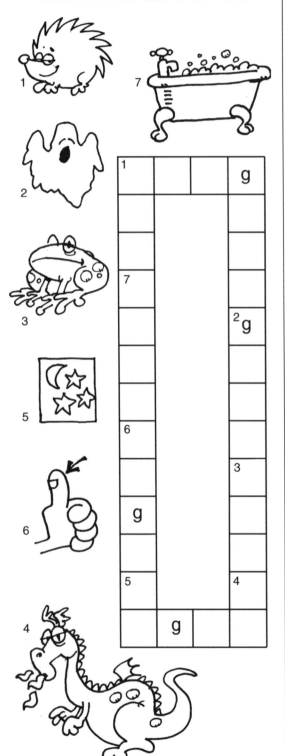

276 **Spelling**

There are two spellings with each picture, check the one you think is correct.

hawse	
horse	

deer	
dear	

donkay	
donkey	

277 **Which line?**

Follow the lines to see which one leads to the anchor.

278 **What weight?**

Count the number of marbles on the scales. Write the number on the other side to make the scales balance.

279 Dotty ladybug
How many spots does the ladybug have?

280 Number code
Do the math to find out what number each symbol is.

🖐	=	
🐌	=	
⭐	=	

🖐	+	🖐	=	6
🐌	×	5	=	20
⭐	−	3	=	5

281 Pole position

Look at the symbols. Each symbol represents a different number of minutes.
Add up the time to see which racing car is fastest.

282 Mystery word

Find the right letters in the grid to fill in the blanks, and you will spell something you see in the sky.

	1	2	3	4	5	6
A	A	N	H	S	K	M
B	S	W	R	S	I	N
C	H	D	A	O	V	G
D	X	H	F	R	T	A
E	P	D	E	Y	T	H
F	P	L	T	I	M	H

___ ___ ___ ___ ___ ___
C6 F2 B5 C2 E3 D4

283 Symmetrical math

Look at the first problem. All the problems must have the same answers as this.

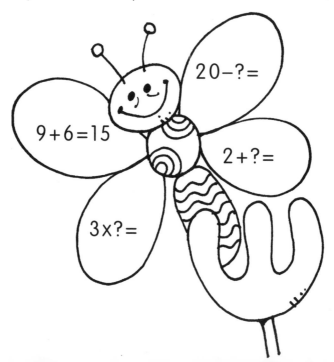

20−?=

9+6=15

2+?=

3×?=

284 Circus, circus!

Look in the wordsearch grid for words to do with the circus. You will find them by reading across or down. Circle the words.

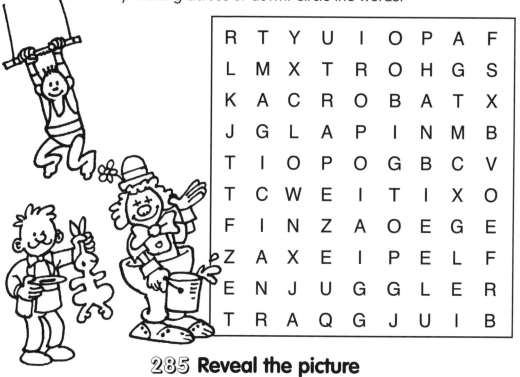

R	T	Y	U	I	O	P	A	F
L	M	X	T	R	O	H	G	S
K	A	C	R	O	B	A	T	X
J	G	L	A	P	I	N	M	B
T	I	O	P	O	G	B	C	V
T	C	W	E	I	T	I	X	O
F	I	N	Z	A	O	E	G	E
Z	A	X	E	I	P	E	L	F
E	N	J	U	G	G	L	E	R
T	R	A	Q	G	J	U	I	B

285 Reveal the picture

Shade in all the spaces marked with a dot to reveal the picture.

286 Flower stand

Look at this flower stand. Can you find a carrot?

287 Where's the party?

Use a mirror to find out where the party is.

the party is at

Sarah's house

_____

_____

288 Wordsearch

Look in the wordsearch grid for six things that are blue. You will find them by reading across or down. Circle the words.

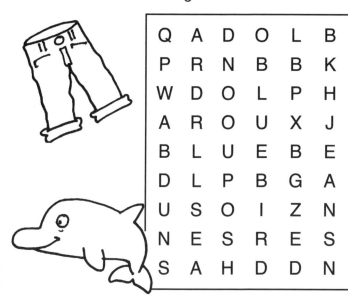

Q	A	D	O	L	B	N	I
P	R	N	B	B	K	H	V
W	D	O	L	P	H	I	N
A	R	O	U	X	J	S	T
B	L	U	E	B	E	L	L
D	L	P	B	G	A	K	A
U	S	O	I	Z	N	Y	I
N	E	S	R	E	S	K	Y
S	A	H	D	D	N	U	O

289 What creature?

Starting with the letter S cross out every other letter. You will end up with the name of a creature.

S C T A K T O E Y R W P M I S L E L C A L R

290 Trivia quiz

Which tree does an acorn come from?

a) oak
b) palm
c) willow

291 Copy and draw

Use the grid to help you draw the other half of the clown,
copying square by square.

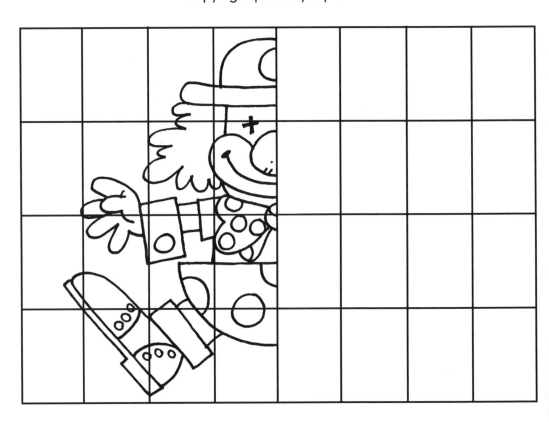

292 Letter square

Starting with the letter T, write every other letter on the lines until you have gone
clockwise around the square twice. You will spell stormy weather.

t	l	h	i	u	g
d					n
g					h
n					d
n					t
a	i	r	n	e	

_____

_____

_____

293 Math puzzle

Do the math in the grid by filling in the missing numbers.

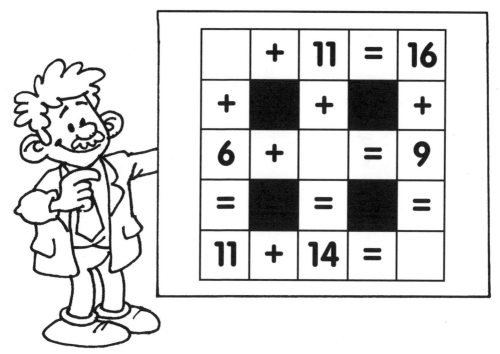

	+	11	=	16
+	■	+	■	+
6	+		=	9
=	■	=	■	=
11	+	14	=	

294 Worm math

Follow the instructions on each worm carefully and do the math.

3 × 2 + 7 − 10 = ▢

7 − 4 × 5 + 2 = ▢

295 Funny faces

Use the outlines below to create you own funny faces.

296 **Dot to dot**

Starting with number 1, draw a line to join the dots and complete the picture.

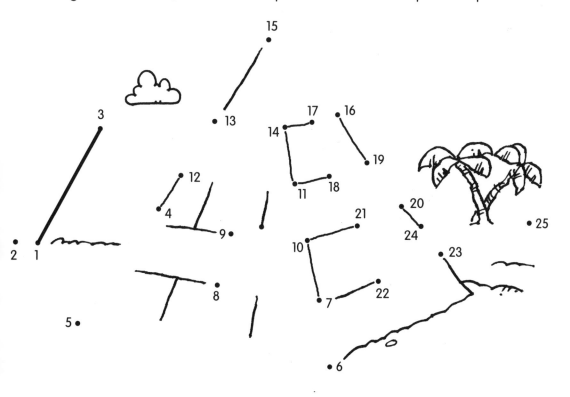

297 **Puzzle wheel**

Write the first letter of each picture in the space in the center of the puzzle wheel. Unscramble the letters and you will spell a new word.

298 Word jumble

Two words have been jumbled together on this line. Can you work out what they are?

S O T C A R T O F I S P H U S

_____   _____

299 Missing piece

Look carefully at this jigsaw puzzle. One piece is missing. Can you see which one fits?

a

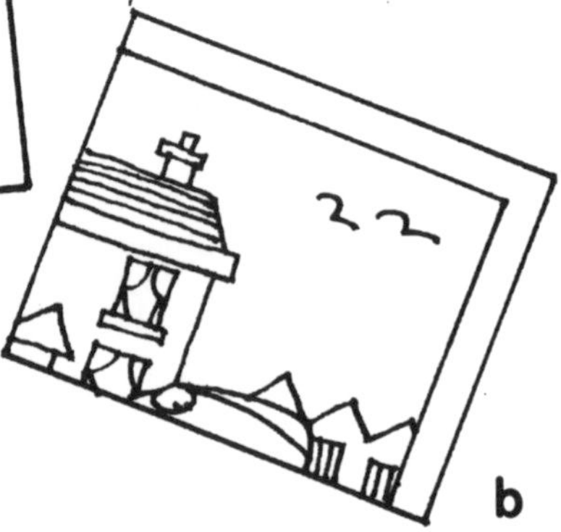

b

c

300 **Hidden word**

Cross out the letters that appear twice in the popsicle. Unscramble the letters to find a flavor.

A O I
L R E
S A M
T S
T I
R
N

301 **Maze**

Help the puppy through the garden to its kennel.

302 Coloring
Color this picture.

303 At the airport
Unscramble the names of these places.

DEPARTURES

OMOOCRC

_____

LIZARB

_____

TRAILAASU

304 **Shadows**

Which shadow belongs to each flower?

305 **Squares**

Which mug has the most squares?

a

b

c

d

306 Lots of suckers

How many suckers in the candy jar?

307 Dot to dot

Starting with number 1, draw a line to join the dots and complete the picture.

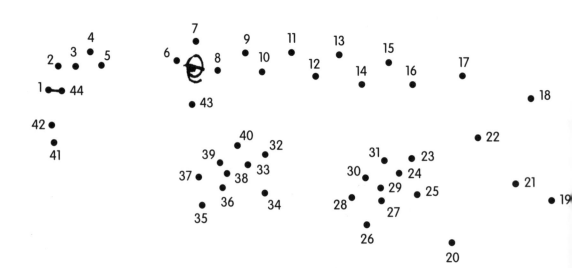

308 Spot the difference

Look carefully at these two pictures. How many differences can you find?

309 Copy and draw
Enlarge the beetle by copying it on to the grid, square by square.

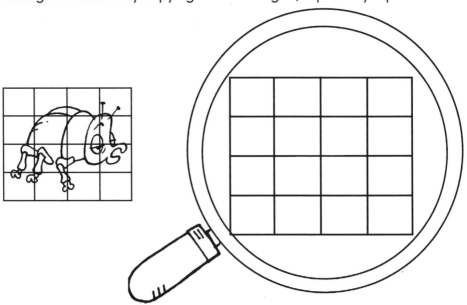

310 Broken plate
This plate has broken into lots of pieces. One piece does not belong to the plate, can you see which it is?

311 Hidden word

Cross out the letters that appear twice in the starfish. The letters that are left spell a sea creature.

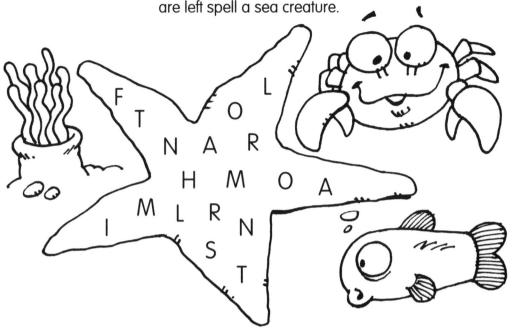

312 Puzzle wheel

Write the first letter of each picture in the space in the center of the puzzle wheel. You will spell a new word.

313 Math puzzle

Do the math in the grid by filling in the missing numbers.

314 How many?

How many new words can you make from the word dinosaur?

DINOSAUR

315 **Word jumble**

Two words have been jumbled together on this line. Can you work out what they are?

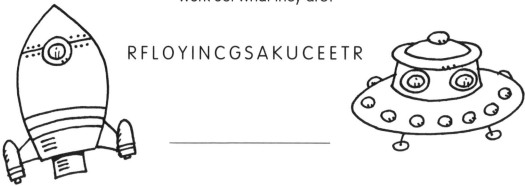

R F L O Y I N C G S A K U C E E T R

_____

_____

316 **Polka-dotted frogs**

Count the polka dots on these frogs and add them up.
Write the total on the lilypad.

317 Who will win the race?

Look at the symbols. Each symbol represents a different number of minutes.
Add them up to see which bird will win the race.

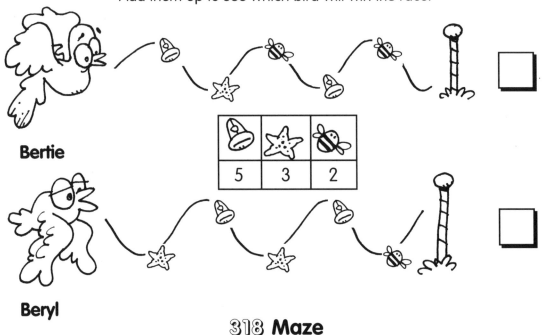

Bertie

🔔	⭐	🐝
5	3	2

Beryl

318 Maze

Help the boy across the field to win the cross-country race.

FINISH

319 Transport wordsearch

Look in the wordsearch grid for these vehicles. You will find them by reading across or down. Draw a ring around the words.

M	N	B	V	C	F	G	H	I
T	U	X	O	B	U	S	C	Y
S	T	A	X	I	O	E	A	B
A	R	P	B	C	F	D	R	C
E	A	K	I	Z	R	E	T	D
O	I	Q	C	C	V	R	E	Z
H	N	J	Y	T	R	U	C	K
O	E	G	C	E	E	G	O	R
K	L	P	L	Y	T	R	E	Q
N	B	Z	E	D	G	H	L	K

320 **Dot to dot**

Starting with number 1, draw a line to join the dots and complete the picture.

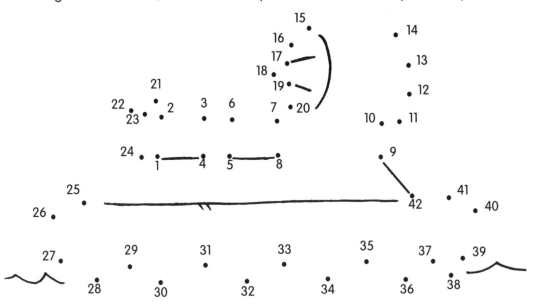

321 **In the garden**

Look at this busy scene. Can you find a hidden worm?

322 **Spot the difference**

Look carefully at these two pictures. How many differences can you find?

323 Copy and draw

Use the grid to help you draw this delicious dessert,
copying square by square.

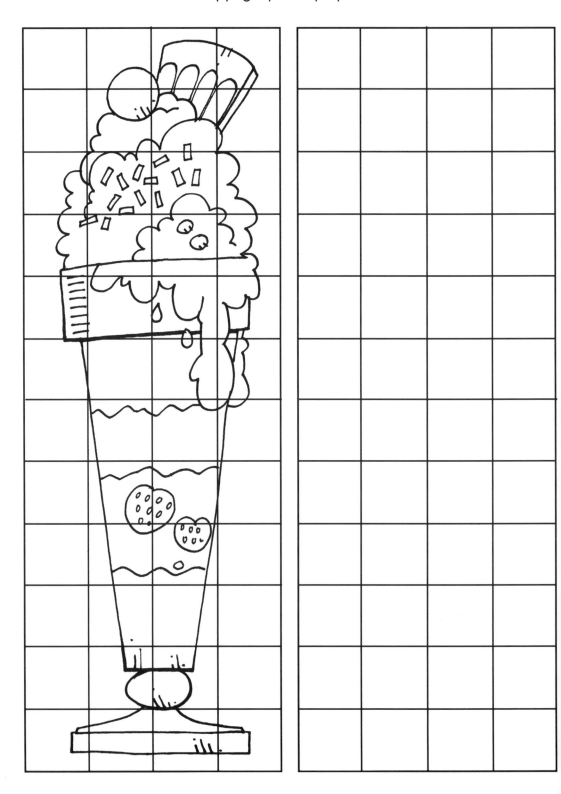

324 Crossword

The pictures of musical instruments are clues. Follow the numbers across and down, and write the words in the grid.

325 In the desert

How many triangles can you count in this picture?

326 What's your name?

Can you unscramble the names of these children?

SSAUN

_____

OSPHJE

_____

HNAYTON

_____

327 Letter wheel

Starting with the letter W, write every other letter on the lines below until you have gone clockwise around the wheel twice.
Then answer the question.

_____

_____

_____

328 Who lives where?

Follow the lines to see where each child lives.

a   b   c

329 Shooting stars

Count how many stars there are.

330 Match the shadows
Draw lines from each shadow to the correct person.

331 Math puzzle
Do the math in the grid by filling in the missing numbers.

3	×		=	12
×	■	×	■	×
3	×	2	=	
=	■	=	■	=
	×	8	=	72

332 **Hidden word**

Cross out the letters that appear twice in the grid to find out who this big footprint belongs to.

A	W	S	Y
E	U	A	H
U	H	T	W
B	I	B	S

333 **Mystery word**

Find the right letters in the grid and fill in the blanks. You will spell the name of a long distance race.

	1	2	3	4	5	6
A	B	J	P	I	N	M
B	A	Y	U	S	Q	Z
C	H	D	E	O	V	G
D	J	L	F	R	T	V
E	U	D	K	Y	T	H
F	P	W	C	A	Q	X

__ __ __ __ __ __ __ __
A6 B1 D4 F4 E5 C1 C4 A5

334 Coloring
Color this picture.

335 Puzzle wheel
Write the first letter of each picture in the space in the center of the puzzle wheel. Unscramble the letters and you will spell a new word.

336 **Odd one out**

Look carefully at these scarecrows. Which one is the odd one?

a

b

c

337 **Spot the difference**

Look carefully at these two pictures. How many differences can you find?

338 Trivia quiz

At what temperature does water freeze?

a) 14°F
b) 50°F
c) 32°F

339 Who is it?

The description of the spy is that he or she does not wear glasses, but does have curly hair, and may be wearing a hat!

a   b   c

Crack the code

Follow the example to crack the code and you'll discover
where they are going.

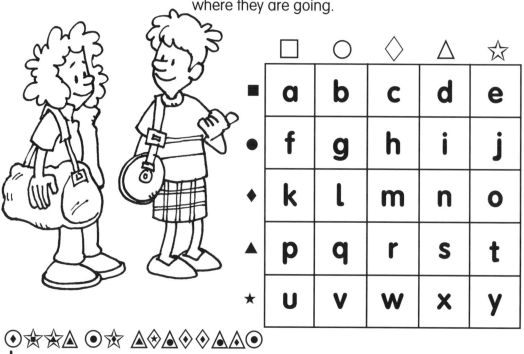

	□	○	◇	△	☆
■	a	b	c	d	e
●	f	g	h	i	j
◆	k	l	m	n	o
▲	p	q	r	s	t
★	u	v	w	x	y

◆ ⊙☆★△ ⊙★ △◆●◆◇ ◇▲◆◉

L _ _ _ _ _ _ _ _ _ _ _ _ _ _ _

341 **Hidden word**

Cross out the letters that appear twice in the grid.
The letters that are left spell a farm animal.

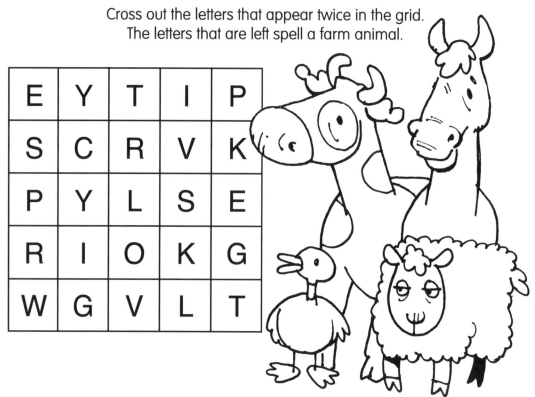

E	Y	T	I	P
S	C	R	V	K
P	Y	L	S	E
R	I	O	K	G
W	G	V	L	T

338 Trivia quiz

At what temperature does water freeze?

a) 14°F
b) 50°F
c) 32°F

339 Who is it?

The description of the spy is that he or she does not wear glasses, but does have curly hair, and may be wearing a hat!

a

b

c

340 Crack the code

Follow the example to crack the code and you'll discover where they are going.

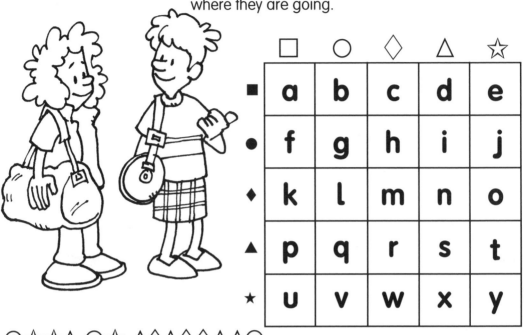

	□	○	◇	△	☆
■	a	b	c	d	e
●	f	g	h	i	j
◆	k	l	m	n	o
▲	p	q	r	s	t
★	u	v	w	x	y

l _ _ _ _ _ _ _ _ _ _ _ _ _ _

341 Hidden word

Cross out the letters that appear twice in the grid. The letters that are left spell a farm animal.

E	Y	T	I	P
S	C	R	V	K
P	Y	L	S	E
R	I	O	K	G
W	G	V	L	T

342 Difficult dominoes

Look carefully at the dominoes. Work out what order they should go in to use them all. Draw the right sequence on the blank dominoes. The first one has been done for you.

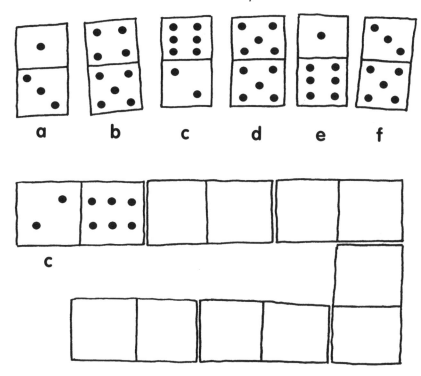

343 Toy addition

Look at the numbers on the toys and do the math. Write the answer on the ball.

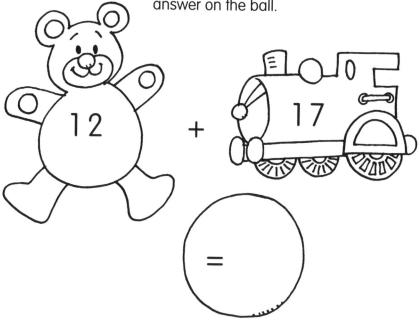

344 Highest

Circle the number you think is the highest.

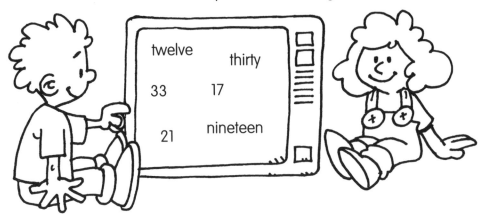

twelve

thirty

33 17

21 nineteen

345 Times square

Multiply these numbers and write the numbers in the grid, following the examples.

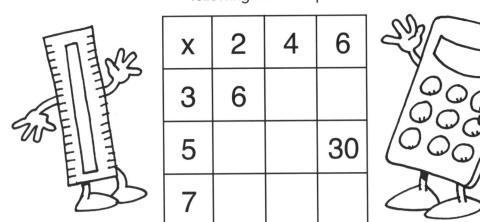

x	2	4	6
3	6		
5			30
7			

346 What a catch!

Count how many fish the fisherman has caught in his net.

347 **Complete the picture**

Parts of this picture are missing. Draw over the dots to complete the picture.

348 **Maze**

Help the prince through the thorny maze to the sleeping princess.

349 **Going shopping**

Look at these pictures and work out the correct order of the story. Write the numbers 1 – 4 in the boxes to put the pictures in the right order.

a

b

c

d

Color this picture.

351 Reveal the picture

Shade in all the spaces marked with a dot to reveal the picture.

352 Which is right?

Look at the picture and read the two statements. Which is true?

a **It was a sunny day and while Peter read his book Joe slept.**

b
It was a sunny day and while Peter was sleeping Joe slept too.

353 Word math

There are twenty people going to the fairground in four cars, how many people in each car?

354 Christmas tree

Draw extra ornaments so there are 12 ornaments on the Christmas tree.

355 **Which one?**

Follow the streams to see which one leads to the waterfall?

1 **2** **3**

356 **Lowest**

Circle the number you think is the lowest.

twenty-one

ten

11

twelve

22

9

14

357 Missing piece

Look carefully at this jigsaw puzzle. One piece is missing.
Can you see which one fits?

358 Flower fun

Count how many flowers there are in each vase and add them up. Write the answers in the boxes.

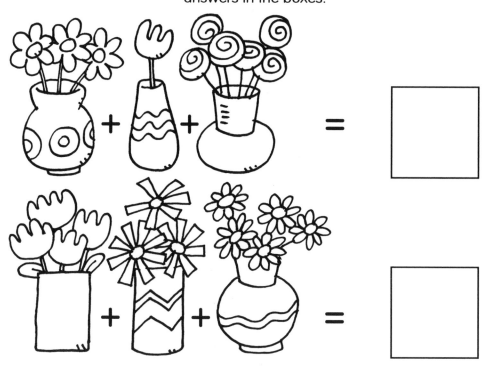

359 Spot the difference

Look carefully at these two pictures. How many differences can you find?

360 **Maze**

Help the squirrel through the park to the tree.

361 My favorite

Follow the lines to see which ice cream each child has.

362 Sailing boat

Copy the sailing boat and draw three more.

363 What time is it?

Look at the times on these clocks and watches, then write the different times on the lines.

3 _____

1 _____

2 _____

4 _____

364 Which house?

James has forgotten where his friend lives, but he remembers that it has the same number of trees as windows and that it has two chimneys. Which number does his friend live at?

2

4

6

8

10

365 Coloring

Color this picture.

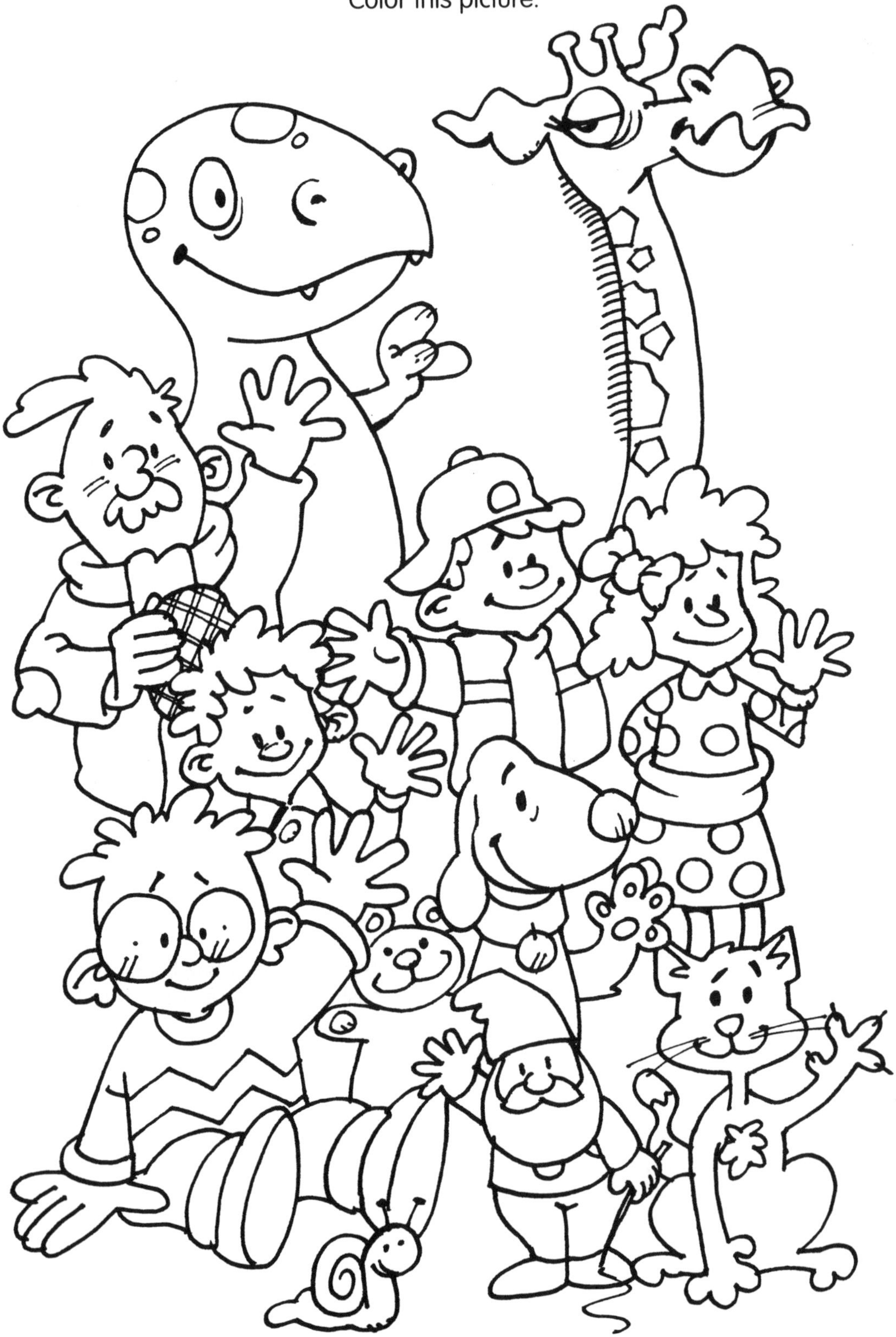

Answers

2. Hey diddle, diddle,
The cat and the fiddle,
The cow jumped over the moon,
The little **dog** laughed to see such fun,
And the **dish** ran away with the **spoon**.

4.

2	+	2	=	4
+	■	–	■	+
9	–	2	=	7
=	■	=	■	=
11	+	0	=	11

5. cat

6. eel, elk, keel, keen, knee, kneel, knelt, knot, leek, lent, let, lone, lose, lot, nest, net, no, not, note, on, one, seen, sleek, sleet, slot, steel, stole, stolen, stone, tee, ten, to, toes, token, ton, tone... can you make any more?

9.

```
Q  W  C  H  U  R  C  H  L
T  J  B  O  D  V  D  X  I
O  S  Z  U  A  F  B  J  G
W  C  P  S  K  J  A  R  H
E  H  V  E  S  E  R  C  T
R  O  X  R  B  H  N  T  H
C  O  T  T  A  G  E  O  O
J  L  A  M  L  H  T  D  U
D  K  T  V  V  N  U  G  S
W  L  R  C  A  S  T  L  E
```

10. 1. suitcase, 2.eggcup, 3. pencil, 4. lightbulb, 5. balloons, 6. sun 7. north, 8. hands

11. b

12. a) John Logie Baird

14. lawnmower, wheelbarrow, butterfly, daffodil

15. cup and saucer, egg and eggcup, teapot

16. c and f are the same

18. 1. cloud different shape
2. pattern on hat
3. straw is shorter
4. shape of flag
5. eyebrow on dog
6. stripe on neck of t-shirt
7. line on lighthouse

19.

```
E  R  K  H  J  N  B  S
S  H  S  W  I  N  G  S
A  O  E  U  Y  W  Q  L
N  Z  E  B  N  J  K  I
D  L  S  J  U  M  H  D
P  L  A  Y  T  I  M  E
I  H  W  E  R  T  Y  U
J  Y  T  R  F  H  J  L
C  H  I  L  D  R  E  N
```

20.

2	×	6	=	12
+	■	–	■	–
3	–	1	=	2
=	■	=	■	=
5	+	5	=	10

21. hello I am a friendly ghost

22. Sleeping Beauty

23. c) 8

24. square

25. tulip

26. baby, bag, balloons, basket, belt, bench, bike, boots, bow, boy, buckle, buggy, bushes... can you find any more?

28. hare – hair
pear – pair
flower – flour

29. hippopotamus

30. ace, are, arrow, as, car, care, case, core, cow, crew, crow, ear, oar, or, ore, race, rare, raw, rear, roar, row, rower, saw, scar, scarce, scare, screw, sea, sew, so, soar, sore, sow, war, was, wear, wore, worse... can you make any more?

31.

15	÷	3	=	5
−		×		+
3	−	2	=	1
=		=		=
12	−	6	=	6

32. bat, cat, fat, hat, mat, pat, rat, sat

38. 9, 18, 27, 36, 45, 54

39. piglet

40. e

41. cat

42. 1. pumpkin, 2. necklace, 3. elbow,
4. window, 5. watch, 6. helicopter,
7. rabbit, 8. top

43. a

44. 4 circles
1 square
7 triangles
2 rectangles

45. James – rollerblades
Susan – doll
Simon – sneakers

48. a and e

49. 23

50. 1. seahorse's head
2. fish's top fin
3. fish's lower fin
4. coral
5. extra anemone
6. crab's eyes

51. Kenya, Norway, Japan

52.

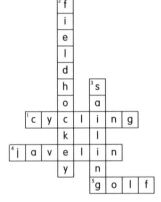

```
W E R T Y U G V
B (D U K E S (C Z
(G O A T) T F O H
V (G S A W E (W F
V X C D O P U Y
K (P I G) Y T R E
E R E W (H D G F
O (S H E E P) Y U
R T V Y (N) K I H
```

53. c) Australia

54. frog

55. chop, clip, clop, colt, cope, core, cot,
creep, crept, crop, echo, eel, either, elite,
epic, heel, help, her, here, hire, hit, hole,
holt, hop, hope, hot, ice, it, itch, let, lie,
lip, liter, lot, opt, or, ore, pelt, pet, pole,
pot, reel, rip, ripe, role, rope, rot, to, top,
tree... can you make any more?

56.

```
           ²f
            i
            e
            l
            d
            h     ³s
            o     a
    ¹c y c l i n g
            k     l
  ⁴j a v e l i n
            y     n
                 ⁵g o l f
```

57. doll, car, ball, teddy, skateboard

58. 0, 12, 24, 36, 48, 60

59. microwave, washing machine,
refrigerator, cupboard

60. Mary had a little **lamb**,
Its fleece was **white** as snow;
And everywhere that Mary went
The lamb was sure to **go**.

62. castle

64. orange

66. 1. strawberry, 2. yogurt,
3. triangles, 4. scarves

67. Little Boy **Blue** come blow your horn,
The sheep's in the meadow,
 the cow's in the **corn**.
Where is the boy that looks after
 the sheep?
He's under a haycock fast **asleep**.

69.

19	−	16	=	3
+	■	−	■	+
2	+	12	=	14
=	■	=	■	=
21	−	4	=	17

70. hat

71. ale, all, alter, ape, art, at, ate, call, cap, cape, crate, crater, ear, eat, ill, it, lace, late, leap, liter, pail, pile, pillar, plate, race, rail, rate, real, tail, tale, tall, tile, till, trace, trail... can you make any more?

74.
```
P R L (B E E C H)
A J G (A E (W M Z
L A H S (F I R) I
M) U O (H A L W N
X H N U O L H Y
(S Y C A M O R E)
E W X O U (W X L
A (O A K) E E J M)
I Y Z O G E A X
```

75. 1. sunflower, 2. rainbow, 3. wigwam, 4. money, 5. yachts

76. b) dinosaur

78. vase of flowers, phone receiver, peppermill

79. hovercraft, airplane, racing car, tractor

81.

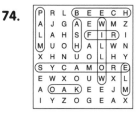

= 3

= 5

= 7

83. octopus, starfish, lobster, crab

84. I had a little nut **tree**,
Nothing would it bear
But a **silver** nutmeg
And a golden **pear**.

85. a and g
b and e
c and f
d is the odd one out

87. Thomas

88. you always end with 5

89. a and d

91. 1. lava on volcano
2. puff of smoke
3. toenail on left dinosaur
4. toe on right dinosaur
5. teeth missing
6. spike on tail missing
7. spot on dinosaur's back
8. leaves on tree

92.
```
Z (F (F L O W E R) 
(F L O W E R) (F N
E (O A F B X (L R
X (W K L I (F O P
F (E V O O L (W R
M (R D W N (O E X
F L K E D (W (R C
B Y Z E M E) X Y
(F L O W E (R) T D
```

93.

3	+	9	=	12
×	■	×	■	÷
12	÷	2	=	6
=	■	=	■	=
36	÷	18	=	2

94. 18

95. Statue of Liberty

96.

x	3	4	5
3	9	12	15
4	12	16	20
5	15	20	25

97. Rachel

98. wolf

99. leaf, lightning, lion, lizard, log ... can you find any more?

101. den, hen, men, pen, ten... can you think of any more?

110. cot, dot, got, hot, jot, lot, not, pot, rot, tot... can you think of any more?

111. a 2, 4, 6, 8, 10, 12
b 5, 10, 15, 20, 25
c 4, 8, 12, 16, 20

112. parrot

113. TUCSON, DALLAS, MEMPHIS, NEW YORK

114. mouse

115. 29 squares
9 circles
1 triangle

116. c

117. the tortoise wins in the fastest time

119.

7	+	4	=	11
x	■	−	■	+
3	x	3	=	9
=	■	=	■	=
21	−	1	=	20

120. January, November, February, March

121. butterfly, worm, bee and 2 caterpillars

124.

```
E W Q T P R Y U
Z X C V L B N M
M E R C U R Y A
E A W D T F A R
B R A E O I O S
C T S A T U R N
V H Q S G V M A
L P N O O T S R
U T A V E N U S
```

125. 1. scarecrow, 2. window, 3. walrus, 4. surfboard, 5. dress

127. b) underground

128. b

129. dictionary, teacher, pencil case

130. rabbit, hedgehog, spider

131. a and e

133. 1. bubbles from glass
2. hair missing from man with hat
3. girl's eyes shut
4. pattern on bow
5. hair different on boy
6. line on glass
7. some of girl's hair missing

135.

12	+	3	=	15
−	■	x	■	÷
6	−	1	=	5
=	■	=	■	=
6	−	3	=	3

136. meet me by the clock

137. Grand Canyon

138. b) 52

139. Africa

140. Sue

144. butterfly

145. an, man, mason, moan, mow, no, now, on, own, saw, snow, so, son, sow, swan, was, woman, won... can you make any more?

147. sack, sausages, scales, scarf, shirt, shoes, shopping bag, spaghetti, ...can you find any more?

149. c

150.

153. 10, 4, 7, 8, 1, 2, 9, 6

154. 6 birds
9 flowers
5 bees

155. c

156. penguin

157. 1. helicopter, 2. rocket, 3. train, 4. nail,
5. lamb, 6. brush

158. b

159. 2 squares
6 circles
2 triangles

160. Jack – beach vacation
Alison – safari
Daniel – skiing

163. a and f

164. 12

165. 1. cloud different shape
2. feathers on owl missing
3. cow's eyes
4. button on farmer's collar
5. farmer's tie
6. steering wheel

166. Pyrenees, Himalayas, Andes

167.

```
D  A  S  D  F  G  Y  O
A  Q  E  T  U  L  I  P
I  P  G  R  F  X  R  M
S  D  T  D  X  O  I  W
Y  P  N  M  R  F  S  A
D  A  F  F  O  D  I  L
S  N  G  X  S  P  O  Q
O  S  E  B  E  Z  Y  N
I  Y  K  P  O  P  P  Y
```

168. b) 6

169. leg

170. 4 + 6 = 10
3 x 9 = 27
14 - 2 = 12
33 ÷ 3 = 11

171. 2 + 8 = 10
10 x 2 = 20
20 ÷ 4 = 5

3 x 3 = 9
9 + 6 = 15
15 ÷ 5 = 3

172. c

174. blackbird, flamingo, ostrich, sparrow

175. 1. glasses
2. ornament stripe
3. shape of bauble on tree
4. stripes on back of glove
5. shape of bow
6. belt buckle
7. loop on bauble

177. tiger

181. giraffe, zebra, monkey, leopard

182.

¹w	o	r	m		
a					⁴s
²s	n	³a	i	l
p		n			u
		t			g

183. dog

184. candy = 7
marbles = 11

185. Tom

186. Tasmanian devil is a ferocious animal
found in Tasmania

187. 1. toucan's beak
2. stripe on toucan's front
3. bush on left
4. pattern on snake
5. gorilla's mouth
6. gorilla's arm

188. dragon

189.

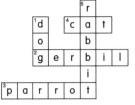

190. kestrel, vulture, eagle, tawny owl

191. b

192. Peter – mountain biking
Zoe – skateboarding
Mark – rollerblading

193. b

196. bent, dent, cent, lent, rent, sent, tent,
went... can you find any more?

197. 12

198. 15

199. Jack-in-the-box

200. sand

201. eagle

202. carrot

204. 11 pens, 1 is a pencil

205. $17 + 13 = 30$

206. a) Canberra

208. pea

209. 12

210.

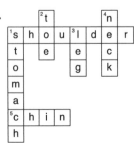

211. c

212. a and f

213. 1 = c
2 = a
3 = b

214. gate is the only one that is not round

215. road

216. c

217. c) November

220. c

221. armadillo, orang-utan, gazelle,
porcupine

223. a and e
b and d
c is the odd one out

224. daisy, dog, doll, dragonfly,
dress, duck, duckling

225. 1. tennis ball
2. button on hat
3. tongue
4. chocolate in ice cream
5. stripe on ball
6. butterfly on dog's nose
7. boy's hair

226.

227.

4	+	9	=	13
+		−		+
10	−	3	=	7
=		=		=
14	+	6	=	20

229. rainbow

230. HOLLAND

233. Mars, Pluto, Venus, Mercury

234.

```
Y  U  K  T  E  R  O  J  R
X  P  A  N  D  A  K  L  I
X  K  N  U  O  O  C  E  K
S  T  G  W  N  M  W  O  L
K  O  A  L  A  B  H  P  O
D  F  R  G  H  I  A  A  P
   S  O  A  W  E  L  R  Z
E  U  O  Y  T  R  E  D  Q
P  G  I  R  A  F  F  E  U
O  V  C  B  M  K  R  A  I
```

235. 1. parrot's beak
2. parrot's tail feathers
3. pirate's eye patch
4. spot missing on headscarf
5. button on pirate's cuff
6. extra coin
7. leaves on tree missing
8. arrow on map

236. a and e

238. 15

239. Tampa, Columbus, Seattle

244. van

245. b) 100

246. Saturn

248. b

249. able, ale, are, arrow, awe, bale, barrow, bear, bee, bow, ear, eel, elbow, ewe, halo, harrow, hear, heel, here, hole, how, law, low, on, owe, rare, raw, rebel, row, wheel, where... can you make any more?

250. c

251. 7 squares
18 circles
9 rectangles

252.

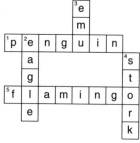

255. a and f
b and d
c and e

256. 15

258. HEAD, BEAD, BEAT, BOAT, BOOT, FOOT

259.

```
Q  W  L  E  M  O  N  V  X
R  E  B  C  X  Z  M  P  P
T  Y  A  P  P  L  E  L  K
U  I  N  D  F  G  L  H  J
O  R  A  N  G  E  O  G  X
O  P  N  S  A  P  N  R  L
A  S  A  T  Y  U  I  A  O
D  F  G  R  E  E  W  P  Q
H  P  E  A  R  M  K  E  N
J  K  L  Z  X  C  V  S  B
```

262. house

264. Mars

265. 1. shape of clown's hat
2. balloon missing
3. clown's bow tie
4. stripes on straw
5. badge on astronaut
6. belt buckle
7. pack missing from astronaut's back

266. motorcycle

267. seaside

268. red

269.

12	+	4	=	16
−		+		−
10	−	2	=	8
=		=		=
2	+	6	=	8

270.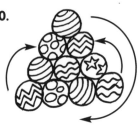

271. 4 + 7 = 11

272. 24

274.

Q	B	W	B	S	L	T	L
I	R	U	B	B	L	E	A
O	I	X	M	K	C	P	D
R	C	R	A	N	E	X	D
N	K	V	S	T	M	X	E
D	S	H	O	V	E	L	R
D	G	S	Z	H	N	B	C
E	A	B	D	F	T	I	O
K	Y	N	X	O	M	J	A

275. 1. hedgehog, 2. ghost, 3. toad,
4. dragon, 5. night, 6. thumb, 7. bath

276. horse, deer, donkey

277. b

278. 6

279. 17

280. 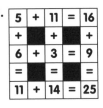 = 3

= 4

= 8

281. car 3

282. glider

283. 20 - 5 = 15
3 x 5 = 15
2 + 13 = 15

284.

R	T	Y	U	I	O	P	A	F
L	M	X	T	R	O	H	G	S
K	A	C	R	O	B	A	T	X
J	G	L	A	P	I	N	M	B
T	I	O	P	O	G	B	C	V
T	C	W	E	I	T	I	X	O
F	I	N	Z	A	O	E	G	E
Z	A	X	E	I	P	E	L	F
E	N	J	U	G	G	L	E	R
T	R	A	Q	G	J	U	I	B

287. the party is at Sarah's house

288.

Q	A	D	O	L	B	N	I
P	R	N	B	B	K	H	V
W	D	O	L	P	H	I	N
A	R	O	U	X	J	S	T
B	L	U	E	B	E	L	L
D	L	P	B	G	A	K	A
U	S	O	I	Z	N	Y	I
N	E	S	R	E	S	K	Y
S	A	H	D	D	N	U	O

289. caterpillar

290. a) oak

292. thunder and lightning

293.

5	+	11	=	16
+		+		+
6	+	3	=	9
=		=		=
11	+	14	=	25

294. 3 x 2 = 6
6 + 7 = 13
13 - 10 = 3

7 - 4 = 3
3 x 5 = 15
15 + 2 = 17

297. rabbit

298. starfish / octopus

299. c

300. lemon

303. Morocco, Brazil, Australia

305. d

306. 12

308. 1. leaves on tree missing
2. man's mouth
3. mug handle
4. opening on tent
5. patch on dog
6. stripe on t-shirt

310. c

311. fish

312. donkey

313.

4	×	4	=	16
÷		÷		÷
2	×	4	=	8
=		=		=
2	×	1	=	2

314. an, and, do, in, is, no, nor, on, our, rod, rain, road, sad, sand, sin, son... can you make any more?

315. rocket, flying saucer

316. 23

317. Bertie

319.

```
M N B V C F G H I
T U X O B U S C Y
S T A X I O E A B
A R P B C F D R C
E A K I Z R E T D
O I Q C C V R E Z
H N J Y T R U C K
O E G C E E G O R
K L P L Y T R E Q
N B Z E D G H L K
```

322. 1. leaf on tree
2. rock from volcano
3. spot on dinosaur's neck
4. leaf on small plant
5. lava on volcano
6. plant on right
7. tooth missing
8. point of tail missing

324.

325. 15

326. Susan, Joseph, Anthony

327. Which is the odd one out?
Answer: b

329. 16

331.

3	×	4	=	12
×		×		×
3	×	2	=	6
=		=		=
9	×	8	=	72

332. yeti

333. marathon

335. rocket

336. b

337. 1. cat's whisker
2. spot on butterfly
3. flower on right
4. dog's teeth
5. tag on dog's collar missing
6. spot on dog

338. c) 32°F

339. b

340. let's go swimming

341. cow

342. c, e, a, f, d, b

343. 12 + 17 = 29

344. 33

345.

x	2	4	6
3	6	12	18
5	10	20	30
7	14	28	42

346. 11

349. 1 = d
2 = b
3 = c
4 = a

352. a

353. five

355. 3

356. 9

357. 3

358. 3 + 1 + 6 = 10
4 + 3 + 5 = 12

359. 1. bow
2. girl's mouth
3. paint splash on table
4. paint splash on picture
5. two paint brushes
6. sun on girl's painting

363. 1. 7.55

 2. 4.00

 3. 9.10

 4. 10.30

364. 4